GW00771516

LAMDA
VERSE AND PROSE
ANTHOLOGY

Volume 19

The LAMDA Verse and Prose Anthology (Volume 19)
First published in 2019 by the
London Academy of Music and Dramatic Art
155 Talgarth Road, London W14 9DA, United Kingdom
Tel: +44 (0)208 834 0530
www.lamda.ac.uk

Edited by Vinota Karunasaagarar

A catalogue record for this book is available from the British Library.

Printed by: Hobbs the Printers Ltd, Totton, Hampshire, SO40 3WX
Page design and layout by: Neil Sutton, Cambridge Design Consultants
Page concept and cover design by: Hudson Fuggle

ISBN: 978-0-9932443-2-2

The LAMDA *Verse and Prose Anthology (Volume 19)* is a collection of verse and prose and is a required publication for Learners taking LAMDA *Graded Examinations in Communication: Speaking Verse and Prose* and the LAMDA *Introductory Examinations Stage One, Stage Two and Stage Three (Solo and Group).*

You may notice that in the case of certain poems or prose extracts, the spelling of some words may vary from piece to piece, representing either standard British or American spelling. This is because we have maintained the spelling found in the original source material.

Contents

Foreword

Growing up in Jamaica, I used to perform poems and plays for school and college functions; it is here I fell in love with the stage. The Jamaican National Festival was a platform for showcasing writing and performing talent and, when a poem I wrote won a medal in the festival, it was officially the start of my writing and performing career. I welcomed the opportunity to take on other personas, to forget my very ordinary existence and to become other, more interesting people, while I was on stage.

When I came to the UK, I toyed with the idea of applying to LAMDA to study drama. I didn't pursue this, so was surprised and delighted to find that not only has one of my poems been included in this anthology, but I was also asked to write the foreword. And what a pleasure it has been to read through this wonderful selection of poems and prose pieces.

The anthology contains poems and extracts of prose, chosen for their Introductory and Communication examinations and, as is to be expected, they are bursting with energy. The pieces have appeal for everyone, not just students. This is a diverse collection, with poems and prose from many different nationalities and for Learners of different ages. Here Samuel Taylor Coleridge, A. E. Housman, Robert Louis Stevenson and Eleanor Farjeon are side by side with Malorie Blackman, Judith Nicholls and Michael Rosen.

It was refreshing to discover some writers I'd not come across before, and some new pieces by well-known authors. I thoroughly enjoyed reading through the anthology and must confess I now have a lot less space in my bookshelves than I had before I started. This anthology will provide students with an abundance of terrific pieces with which to display their talent; and my hope is that Learners will feel immense enjoyment from browsing through the anthology when choosing pieces for their examinations.

Valerie Bloom (MBE)

Thanks

LAMDA Examinations would like to thank all of the authors, publishers and agents who made the development of this anthology possible. Special thanks are also due to Faye Carmichael, Elaine Elliot, Vivien Heilbron, Zoe Little, Linda Macrow, Eleanor McLeod, Wyn Richards, Michael Stone and Christina Williams.

SOLO INTRODUCTORY

Solo Introductory:
Stage 1

Titles in Solo Introductory: Stage 1

Clouds

My Hat!

Mix a Pancake

The Red Boat

Sounds Good!

My Puppy

Clouds

Little bits of cloud

High in the sky,

Little bits of cloud

Float slowly by,

Count all the bits

And that will be,

The number of fishes

There are in the sea.

By Valerie Bloom

My Hat!

Here's my hat.
It holds my head,
the thoughts I've had
and the things I've read.

It keeps out the wind.
It keeps off the rain.
It hugs my hair
and warms my brain.

There's me below it,
the sky above it.
It's my lid.
And I love it.

By Tony Mitton

Mix a Pancake

Mix a pancake,

Stir a pancake,

Pop it in the pan;

Fry the pancake,

Toss the pancake–

Catch it if you can.

By Christina Rossetti

The Red Boat

Here goes the sun
slowly sailing by,

like a red boat
on the ocean of the sky.

There goes the sun
all the day through,
a red boat sailing
across its sea of blue.

By Wes Magee

Sounds Good!

Sausage sizzles,

crispbreads crack;

hot dogs hiss

and flapjacks snap!

Bacon boils

and fritters fry;

apples squelch

in apple pie.

Baked beans bubble,

gravy grumbles;

popcorn pops,

and stomach rumbles...

I'M HUNGRY!

By Judith Nicholls

My Puppy

My puppy is so naughty

He always runs away

He never hears me when I call

Or stops when I say 'STAY!'

The only time he listens

And stops tearing down the street

Is when he hears his favourite word

'TREAT!'

'TREAT!'

'TREAT!!!'

By Debra Bertulis

GROUP INTRODUCTORY

Group Introductory:
Stage 1

Titles in Group Introductory: Stage 1

Two or Three Posies

Ladybug, Ladybug

If I Were King

Two or Three Posies

Two or three posies
With two or three simples –
Two or three noses
With two or three pimples –
Two or three wise men
And two or three ninny's –
Two or three purses
And two or three guineas –
Two or three raps
At two or three doors –
Two or three naps
Of two or three hours –
Two or three cats
And two or three mice –
Two or three sprats
At a very great price –
Two or three sandies
And two or three tabbies –
Two or three dandies
And two Mrs – mum!
Two or three smiles
And two or three frowns –
Two or three miles
To two or three towns –
Two or three pegs
For two or three bonnets –
Two or three dove eggs
To hatch into sonnets.

By John Keats

Ladybug, Ladybug

Ladybug, Ladybug
Stay right here.
Don't fly home,
You have nothing to fear.

Your children are sleeping.
Your husband is shopping.
Your father is sweeping.
Your mother is mopping.

Your grandma is strumming.
Your grandpa is clapping.
Your auntie is humming.
Your uncle is napping.

Your brother is riding.
Your sister is cooking.
Your niece is hiding.
Your nephew is looking.

Ladybug, Ladybug
Stay right here.
Don't fly home,
You have nothing to fear.

By John Himmelman

If I Were King

I often wish I were a King,
And then I could do anything.

If only I were King of Spain,
I'd take my hat off in the rain.

If only I were King of France,
I wouldn't brush my hair for aunts.

I think, if I were King of Greece,
I'd push things off the mantelpiece.

If I were King of Norroway,
I'd ask an elephant to stay.

If I were King of Babylon,
I'd leave my button gloves undone.

If I were King of Timbuctoo,
I'd think of lovely things to do.

If I were King of anything,
I'd tell the soldiers, 'I'm the King!'

By A. A. Milne

Solo Introductory:
Stage 2

Titles in Solo Introductory: Stage 2

Did You Ever Play Tag with a Tiger?

Did you ever play tag with a tiger,

Or ever play boo with a bear;

Did you ever put rats in the rain-barrel

To give poor old Granny a scare?

It's fun to play tag with a tiger,

It's fun for the bear to say 'boo,'

But if rats are found in the rain-barrel

Old Granny will put you in too.

By Leroy F. Jackson

Hello! Hello!

Hello! hello!

Come down below,--

It's lovely and cool

Out here in the pool;

On a lily-pad float

For a nice green boat.

Here we sit and sing

In a pleasant ring;

Or leap frog play,

In the jolliest way.

Our games have begun,

Come join in the fun.

By Louisa M. Alcott

Down Behind the Dustbin

Down behind the dustbin
I met a dog called Ted.
'Leave me alone,' he says,
'I'm just going to bed.'

Down behind the dustbin
I met a dog called Roger.
'Do you own this bin?' I said.
'No. I'm only a lodger.'

Down behind the dustbin
I met a dog called Sue.
'What are you doing here?' I said.
'I've got nothing else to do.'

By Michael Rosen

To Catch a Fish

It takes more than a wish

to catch a fish

you take the hook

you add the bait

you concentrate

and then you wait

you wait   you wait

but not a bite

the fish don't have

an appetite

so tell them what

good bait you've got

and how your bait

can hit the spot

this works a whole

lot better than

a wish

if you really

want to catch

a fish

By Eloise Greenfield

The Folk Who Live in Backward Town

The folk who live in Backward Town

Are inside out and upside down.

They wear their hats inside their heads

And go to sleep beneath their beds.

They only eat the apple peeling

And take their walks across the ceiling.

By Mary Ann Hoberman

Hot Cross Buns

I don't think a hot cross bun

Looks very cross at all.

It has a sort of smiley face,

And eyes of currants small.

Its cheeks are sweet and sticky,

And it tastes just…well…oh yum!

I'm smiling now because I've eaten

Another hot cross bun!

By Eleanor McLeod

Group Introductory:
Stage 2

Titles in Group Introductory: Stage 2

Is a Bee a Good Thing to be?

Our Club

Diplodocus

Is a Bee a Good Thing to be?

I like the ocelot a lot,
Hyenas are a laugh.
I wanna be a wallaby
Or tall, like a giraffe.

What fun to be a chimpanzee.
A cockatoo would do.
Or flutter like a butterfly,
Hop like a kangaroo.

The pelican is elegant,
A llama is alarmed.
Tarantula's gargantuan.
Can cobras be uncharmed?

The hippopotamus likes mud,
I bet that cheetahs cheat,
And elephants just love to stomp.
Chinchillas' chins are sweet.

But all the creatures I have named
Are living in the wild.
I think perhaps I'd rather be
Just me, a human child.

By Ellen Weeks

Our Club

We're going to have the mostest fun!
It's going to be a club;
And no one can belong to it
But Dot and me and Bub.

We thought we'd have a Reading Club,
But couldn't 'cause, you see,
Not one of us knows how to read—
Not Dot nor Bub nor me.

And then we said a Sewing Club,
But thought we'd better not;
'Cause none of us knows how to sew—
Not me nor Bub nor Dot.

And so it's just a Playing Club,
We play till time for tea;
And, oh, we have the bestest times!
Just Dot and Bub and me.

By Carolyn Wells

Diplodocus

Diplodocus plodded along on the trail
on four massive thundering feet,
it had a long neck, and a serpentine tail,
and Diplodocus plodded along long ago,
Diplodocus plodded along.

Diplodocus feasted from morning till night,
it did almost nothing but eat,
it couldn't go far without taking a bite,
and Diplodocus plodded along long ago,
Diplodocus plodded along.

Diplodocus needed to stay on its toes,
and watch with its skyscraper eyes,
for it was surrounded by ravenous foes,
and Diplodocus plodded along long ago,
Diplodocus plodded along.

Diplodocus never could move very fast,
Because of its ponderous size,
it lived long ago, and its time is now past,
and Diplodocus plodded along long ago,
Diplodocus plodded along.

By Jack Prelutsky

Solo Introductry:
Stage 3

Titles in Solo Introductory: Stage 3

Riddle

Caterpillars

There isn't Time

Room with a View

The Backwards Bus

Discretion

Riddle

Allow me to describe myself,

I live upon a dusty shelf,

With other sorts who do the same.

I have a title to my name,

Yet wear a jacket without sleeves.

I'm not a plant but I have leaves.

(It's also true I'm not a tree,

Though that is what I used to be.)

I'm full of words but cannot speak,

I sometimes vanish for a week

And then return to my dear nook.

You've guessed it – I'm a library book!

By Colin West

Caterpillars

They came like dewdrops overnight
Eating every plant in sight,
Those nasty worms with legs that crawl
So creepy up the garden wall,
Green prickly fuzz to hurt and sting
Each unsuspecting living thing.
How I hate them!   Oh, you know
I'd love to squish them with my toe.
But then I see past their disguise,
Someday they'll all be butterflies.

By Brod Bagert

There isn't Time

There isn't time, there isn't time

To do the things I want to do –

With all the mountain tops to climb

And all the woods to wander through

And all the seas to sail upon

And everywhere there is to go,

And all the people, every one,

Who live upon the earth to know.

There's only time, there's only time

To know a few, to do a few,

And then sit down and make a rhyme

About the rest I want to do.

By Eleanor Farjeon

Room with a View

I live in a room by the sea,

where the view is great and the food is free.

Some of the tenants come and go.

Some I eat, if they're too slow.

One end of me is firmly locked.

The other end just gently rocks.

I live in a room by the sea.

It's perfect for an anemone.

By Stephen Swinburne

The Backwards Bus

Miss Donna drives our school bus
But today she called in sick.
So we had to have a substitute;
They sent a guy named Rick.

Well, I think that for Rick to drive a bus
Today must be the first
Cause he simply couldn't get the thing
To shift out of reverse.

Now the bus looked pretty crazy
When it pulled up to my stop.
All the kids were facing backwards
As the air brakes went pop-pop.

I climbed up beside the driver
Thinking this was kind of cool
And looked back out of the front window
Until we got to school.

By Martha Cheney

Discretion

A man with a nickel,

A sword, and a sickle,

A pipe, and a paper of pins

Set out for the Niger

To capture a tiger—

And that's how my story begins.

When he saw the wide ocean,

He soon took a notion

'T would be nicer to stay with his friends.

So he traded his hat

For a tortoise-shell cat—

And that's how the chronicle ends.

By Leroy F. Jackson

Group Introductory:
Stage 3

Titles in Group Introductory: Stage 3

Good Morning, Mr Croco-doco-dile

Good Morning, Mr Croco-doco-dile,
And how are you today?
I like to see your croco-smoco-smile
In your croco-woco-way.

From the tip of your beautiful croco-toco-tail
To your croco-hoco-head
You seem to me so croco-stoco-still
As if you are croco-doco-dead.

Perhaps if I touch your croco-cloco-claw,
Or your croco-snoco-snout,
Or get up to your croco-joco-jaw,
I shall very soon find out.

But suddenly I croco-soco-see
In your croco-oco-eye
A curious kind of croco-gloco-gleam,
So, I just don't think I'll try.

Forgive me, Mr Croco-doco-dile
But it's time I was away.
Let's talk a little croco-woco-while
Another croco-doco-day.

By Charles Causley

Schoolspeak

's cool, man,

It's the best,

Gotta keep your interest

Talkin' is the name of the game

And if you wanna play

You gotta speak the same:

SCHOOLSPEAK,

's cool, man,

Understand me if you can.

P.E.'s brill,

Maths is vile,

Maths, man, it ain't my style.

Art's a doddle,

R.E.'s a doss,

Gotta show 'em who's the boss:

SCHOOLSPEAK,

's cool, man,

It's the lingo they wanna ban.

Science is grotty,

Drama's dead good,

History I'd skive, if I could.

English is ace,

French is a bind,

I'd love to leave this class behind:

SCHOOLSPEAK,

's cool, man,

's all part of my master plan.

Miss is magic,

Sir's a pain,

Head's a wally, Librarian's plain,

Dinners are skill,

Homework's a drag

I'm tellin' you school ain't my bag.

SCHOOLSPEAK,

SCHOOL, MAN,

's cool.

By Ray Mather

Brian's Picnic

We've...

cheese rolls, chicken rolls,

beef rolls, ham;

Choose now, quickly, Brian –

bacon, beans or Spam?

I WANT A DOUGHNUT!

We've...

Egg and cress and sausages,

Good old lettuce leaf;

Come on, Brian, take some now –

There's turkey, tuna, beef...

I WANT A DOUGHNUT!

We've...

Treacle tart and apple tart,

Biscuits, blackberries, cake –

Take which one you feel like,

Brian, come along now, take!

I WANT A DOUGHNUT!

There's...

jelly next or trifle,

everything must go!

Quickly, Brian, pass your plate –

is it yes or no?

I WANT A DOUGHNUT!

LAST CHANCE!

We've…

Sponge cake, fruit cake,

eat it *any* way!

Peanut butter, best rump steak…

what is that you say?

I WANT A DOUGHNUT!

By Judith Nicholls

Entry Level

Speaking Verse and Prose

Titles in Entry Level Speaking Verse and Prose

Some One

Someone came knocking

At my wee, small door;

Someone came knocking,

I'm sure—sure—sure;

I listened, I opened,

I looked to left and right,

But nought there was a-stirring

In the still dark night;

Only the busy beetle

Tap-tapping in the wall,

Only from the forest

The screech-owl's call,

Only the cricket whistling

While the dewdrops fall,

So I know not who came knocking,

At all, at all, at all.

By Walter de la Mare

The Star

Twinkle, twinkle, little star,
How I wonder what you are!
Up above the world so high,
Like a diamond in the sky.

When the blazing sun is gone,
When he nothing shines upon,
Then you show your little light,
Twinkle, twinkle, all the night.

Then the trav'ller in the dark,
Thanks you for your tiny spark,
He could not see which way to go,
If you did not twinkle so.

In the dark blue sky you keep,
And often thro' my curtains peep,
For you never shut your eye,
Till the sun is in the sky.

'Tis your bright and tiny spark,
Lights the trav'ller in the dark:
Tho' I know not what you are,
Twinkle, twinkle, little star.

By Ann and Jane Taylor

Have You Ever Seen?

Have you ever seen a sheet on a river bed?

Or a single hair from a hammer's head?

Has the foot of a mountain any toes?

And is there a pair of garden hose?

Does the needle ever wink its eye?

Why doesn't the wing of a building fly?

Can you tickle the ribs of a parasol?

Or open the trunk of a tree at all?

Are the teeth of a rake ever going to bite?

Have the hands of a clock any left or right?

Can the garden plot be deep and dark?

And what is the sound of the birch's bark?

By Anonymous

The Robin Makes a Laughing Sound

The robin makes a laughing sound.

It makes me stop and look around

to see just what the robin sees—

fresh new leaves on twigs of trees,

a strong, high branch on which to rest,

a safe dry ledge to hold its nest.

The robin makes a laughing sound.

I stop. I always look around.

By Sallie Wolf

Pop-Corn

Pop! Pop!—Poppetty-pop!

Shake and rattle and rattle and shake

The golden grains as they bounce and break

To fluffy puffiness—*Poppetty-pop!*

Bursting and banging the popper's top!

Poppetty-pop!

Pop! Pop!

The yellow kernels, oh, see them grow

White as cotton or flakes of snow!

Pop! Pop!

O-ho, how they frolic and fly about

And turn themselves suddenly inside out!

Pop-pop-poppetty! Pop-pop-pop!

The popper's full and we'll have to stop;

Pile the bowl with the tempting treat,

Children, come, it is time to eat!

By Evaleen Stein

The Moon

The moon has a face like the clock in the hall;
She shines on thieves on the garden wall,
On streets and fields and harbour quays,
And birdies asleep in the forks of the trees.

The squalling cat and the squeaking mouse,
The howling dog by the door of the house,
The bat that lies in bed at noon,
All love to be out by the light of the moon.

But all of the things that belong to the day
Cuddle to sleep to be out of her way;
And flowers and children close their eyes
Till up in the morning the sun shall arise.

By Robert Louis Stevenson

The Dodo

The doleful Dodo lay in bed
And feebly said:
'My muscles ache,
My kidneys quake,
My feathers shake,
I've noises in my head.
I'm very sick'
      He said.

Then turning to the wall he blinked,
And whispered in a voice quite indistinct,
'It's really not surprising I'm extinct'.

By Peter Wesley-Smith

Riches

I have no riches but my thoughts,

Yet these are wealth enough for me;

My thoughts of you are golden coins

Stamped in the mint of memory;

And I must spend them all in song,

For thoughts, as well as gold, must be

Left on the hither side of death

To gain their immortality.

By Sara Teasdale

Level 1 Speaking Verse and Prose:

Grade 1

Titles in Level 1 Speaking Verse and Prose: Grade 1

Bed in Summer

The Sandman

Step Dad

The African Lion

Migration

I Tried to Do My Homework

Answer to a Child's Question

Carousel

Bed in Summer

In winter I get up at night
And dress by yellow candle-light.
In summer, quite the other way,
I have to go to bed by day.

I have to go to bed and see
The birds still hopping on the tree,
Or hear the grown-up people's feet
Still going past me in the street.

And does it not seem hard to you,
When all the sky is clear and blue,
And I should like so much to play,
To have to go to bed by day?

By Robert Louis Stevenson

The Sandman

The Sandman! hark, I hear him!
He's coming up the stair,
And everybody near him
Is nodding, I declare!
He's peeping in the door now,
And first of all he spies,
As he has done before now,
The little children's eyes!
Then quickly does he throw it,
His golden sleepy-sand,
And all, before they know it,
Are off for sleepy-land!

By Evaleen Stein

Step Dad

My Step Dad takes me to the park
He pushes me on the swing
And chats to me as we sit on the bench
About life and everything.

He says he really loves my Mum
And he really loves me too
And asks what I'd like for tea tonight
And if sausage and mash will do.

My Step Dad takes me to the park
We play as time flies by
My Step Dad is my second Dad
How lucky, how lucky am I?

By Debra Bertulis

The African Lion

To meet a bad lad on the African waste
Is a thing that a lion enjoys;
But he rightly and strongly objects to the taste
Of good and uneatable boys.

When he bites off a piece of a boy of that sort
He spits it right out of his mouth,
And retires with a loud and dissatisfied snort
To the east, or the west, or the south.

So lads of good habits, on coming across
A lion, need feel no alarm,
For they know they are sure to escape with the loss
Of a leg, or a head, or an arm.

By A. E. Housman

Migration

Where do birds go

When the ground's covered in snow?

Far, far away,

Where the wild lions play

And the sun's always hot,

Elephants flop,

Baboons howl at night,

The moon's large and bright,

And crickets form choirs

Around evening fires –

That's where they fly,

Through the dark winter sky,

That's where they go

When the ground's covered in snow.

By Richard Macwilliam

I Tried to Do My Homework

I tried to do my homework
but a show was on TV.
A song was on the radio.
A friend was texting me.

My email chimed, and so, of course,
I had to look at that.
It linked me to a video
of someone's silly cat.

I watched a dozen videos,
and then I played a game.
I almost didn't hear her
when my mother called my name.

I looked up at the clock
and it was time to go to bed.
I didn't get my homework done;
just other stuff instead.

I hope my teacher listens
to the cause of my inaction.
It's really not my fault the world
is just one big distraction.

By Kenn Nesbitt

Answer to a Child's Question

Do you ask what the birds say? The sparrow, the dove,

The linnet, and thrush say, 'I love and I love!'

In the winter they're silent, the wind is so strong;

What it says, I don't know, but it sings a loud song.

But green leaves and blossoms, and sunny warm weather,

And singing, and loving, all come back together.

Then the lark is so brimful of gladness and love,

The green fields below him, the blue sky above,

That he sings, and he sings, and forever sings he—

'I love my Love, and my Love loves me!'

By Samuel Taylor Coleridge

Carousel

On thin golden poles
gliding up, sliding down,
a kingdom of horses
goes spinning around.

Jumper, Brown Beauty,
Dark Thunder, Sir Snow,
a medley of ponies
parade in a row.

Settled in saddles,
their riders hold on
to reins of soft leather
while circling along

on chestnut or charcoal,
on sleek Arctic white,
on silver they gallop
in place day and night.

Such spinning is magic,
(to dream as you sail)
with lavender saddle
and ebony tail,

whirling to music
in moonlight, spellbound,
galloping, galloping,
merrily go round.

By Rebecca Kai Dotlich

Level 1 Speaking Verse and Prose:
Grade 2 – Verse

Titles in Level 1 Speaking Verse and Prose:
Grade 2 – Verse

The Sloth

In moving-slow he has no Peer.

You ask him something in his Ear,

He thinks about it for a Year;

And, then, before he says a Word

There, upside down (unlike a Bird),

He will assume that you have Heard –

A most Ex-as-per-at-ing Lug.

But should you call his manner Smug,

He'll sigh and give his Branch a Hug;

Then off again to Sleep he goes,

Still swaying gently by his Toes,

And you just *know* he knows he knows.

By Theodore Roethke

Baby Ate a Microchip

Baby ate a microchip,
Then grabbed a bottle, took a sip.
He swallowed it and made a beep,
And now he's thinking pretty deep.

He's downloading his ABCs
And calculating 1-2-3s.
He's memorizing useless facts
While doing Daddy's income tax.

He's processing, and now he thrives
On feeding his internal drives.
He's throwing fits, and now he fights
With ruthless bits and toothless bytes.

He must be feeling very smug.
But hold on, Baby caught a bug.
Attempting to reboot in haste,
He accidentally got erased!

By Neal Levin

A Teacher's Lament

Don't tell me the cat ate your math sheet,
And your spelling words went down the drain,
And you couldn't decipher your homework,
Because it was soaked in the rain.

Don't tell me you slaved for hours
On the project that's due today,
And you would have had it finished
If your snake hadn't run away.

Don't tell me you lost your eraser,
And your worksheets and pencils, too,
And your papers are stuck together
With a great big glob of glue.

I'm tired of all your excuses;
They are really a terrible bore.
Besides, I forgot my own work,
At home in my study drawer.

By Kalli Dakos

Up-Hill

Does the road wind up-hill all the way?
Yes, to the very end.
Will the day's journey take the whole long day?
From morn to night, my friend.

But is there for the night a resting-place?
A roof for when the slow dark hours begin.
May not the darkness hide it from my face?
You cannot miss that inn.

Shall I meet other wayfarers at night?
Those who have gone before.
Then must I knock, or call when just in sight?
They will not keep you standing at that door.

Shall I find comfort, travel-sore and weak?
Of labour you shall find the sum.
Will there be beds for me and all who seek?
Yea, beds for all who come.

Christina Rossetti

Jaguar

some say

I'm now almost

extinct in this park

but the people

who say this

don't know

that by smelling

the orchids

in the trees

they're sensing

the fragrance

of my chops

that by hearing

the rumbling

of the waterfalls

they're listening

to my ancestors'

great roar

that by observing

the constellations

of the night sky

they're gazing

at the star spots

on my fur

that I am and

always will be

the wild

untamed

living spirit

of this jungle

By Francisco X. Alarcón

A Marvel

An old astronomer there was

Who lived up in a tower,

Named Ptolemy Copernicus

Flammarion McGower.

He said: 'I can prognosticate

With estimates correct;

And when the skies I contemplate,

I know what to expect.

When dark'ning clouds obscure my sight,

I think perhaps 'twill rain;

And when the stars are shining bright,

I know 'tis clear again.'

And then abstractedly he scanned

The heavens, hour by hour,

Old Ptolemy Copernicus

Flammarion McGower.

By Carolyn Wells

The Letter A

The letter A is awesome!

It simply is the best.

Without an A, you could not get

an A+ on a test.

You'd never see an acrobat

or eat an apple pie.

You couldn't be an astronaut

or kiss your aunt goodbye.

An antelope would not exist.

An ape would be unknown.

You'd never hear a person

say 'Afraid' or 'All Alone'.

The A's in avocado

would completely disappear

and certain words would be forgot

like 'ankle', 'arm', and 'ear'.

Without the A, you couldn't aim

an arrow in the air.

You wouldn't ask for apricots

or almonds at a fair.

Aruba and Australia

would be missing from a map.

You'd never use an ATM,

an apron, or an app.

The arctic fox and aardvark

would be absent from the zoo,

and vowels, as you know them,

would be E, I, O, and U.

There wouldn't be an A chord

on the instruments you play.

Let's appreciate, admire,

and applaud the letter A!

By Darren Sardelli

Little Trotty Wagtail

Little trotty wagtail he went in the rain

And tittering tottering sideways he near got straight again

He stooped to get a worm and look'd up to catch a fly

And then he flew away e're his feathers they were dry

Little trotty wagtail he waddled in the mud

And left his little foot marks trample where he would

He waddled in the water pudge and waggle went his tail

And chirrup up his wings to dry upon the garden rail

Little trotty wagtail you nimble all about

And in the dimpling water pudge you waddle in and out

Your home is nigh at hand and in the warm pigsty

So little Master Wagtail I'll bid you a 'Good bye'

By John Clare

Level 1 Speaking Verse and Prose:
Grade 2 – Prose

Titles in Level 1 Speaking Verse and Prose:
Grade 2 – Prose

The Town Mouse and the Country Mouse

Operation Gadgetman!

Olivia's First Term

The Many Worlds of Albie Bright

Sophie's Snail

Five Go Adventuring Again

Arsenic for Tea

Black Beauty

The Town Mouse and the Country Mouse

Now you must know that a Town Mouse once upon a time went on a visit to his cousin in the country. He was rough and ready, this cousin, but he loved his town friend and made him heartily welcome. Beans and bacon, cheese and bread, were all he had to offer, but he offered them freely. The Town Mouse rather turned up his long nose at this country fare, and said: 'I cannot understand, Cousin, how you can put up with such poor food as this, but of course you cannot expect anything better in the country; come you with me and I will show you how to live. When you have been in town a week you will wonder how you could ever have stood a country life.'

No sooner said than done: the two mice set off for the town and arrived at the Town Mouse's residence late at night. 'You will want some refreshment after our long journey,' said the polite Town Mouse, and took his friend into the grand dining-room. There they found the remains of a fine feast, and soon the two mice were eating up jellies and cakes and all that was nice. Suddenly they heard growling and barking. 'What is that?' said the Country Mouse. 'It is only the dogs of the house,' answered the other. 'Only!' said the Country Mouse. 'I do not like that music at my dinner.' Just at that moment the door flew open, in came two huge mastiffs, and the two mice had to scamper down and run off. 'Good-bye, Cousin,' said the Country Mouse, 'What! going so soon?' said the other. 'Yes,' he replied;

'Better beans and bacon in peace than cakes and ale in fear.'

By Aesop

Operation Gadgetman!

BOOM! WHIIZZ! KER-BOOOM!

The whole house shook and the windows rattled violently. Gadgetman was at it again! Beans was still for only a moment.

She ran out of the bathroom and dashed downstairs, her toothbrush in her hand.

'Dad! Dad, what's going on?' Beans yelled.

A high-pitched whistle shrieked through the house again. Beans ran into the kitchen.

BOOOOM! WHIZZZ!

'Eeek!' Beans threw herself down on to the kitchen floor.

Only just in time, too! A small red-and-yellow doobry-whatsit whizzed through the open kitchen window and shot over her head, before veering left to crash into a box of cornflakes.

BOOOOOOM!

Beans shook her head as she got to her feet. Dad could blow up his workroom if he wanted to – and he often did! – but did he have to blow up the kitchen as well? Dad's workroom was at the bottom of the garden, but there were times when the bottom of the garden wasn't far enough away. Beans didn't mind her dad being an inventor – much! – but did he have to make so much noise about it?

By Malorie Blackman

Olivia's First Term

'It was my big chance. I was going to do a solo. I wanted to make my mum really proud of me,' she whispered. 'She'll be so disappointed. I'm glad she wasn't here to see me like this.' Olivia squeezed Georgia's clammy hand.

'You'll get other chances,' said Olivia kindly. 'And I bet your mum's already proud of you; she must be if you were chosen to do a solo.' But Georgia had closed her eyes and Olivia was moved aside by the arrival of Sebastian Shaw, the acting teacher, and India Taylor, the senior dancing teacher, who gently pulled Georgia to her feet and helped her limp away.

As they moved off, Olivia overheard Sebastian ask Georgia how the accident had happened. A look of confusion mixed with dismay crossed Georgia's face.

'I don't know,' she said miserably. 'Somebody...no.' She shook her head, which felt a bit fuzzy. 'I must've slipped. One minute I was peeping out of the curtains and the next I was on the floor in front of the stage.'

Miss Taylor tutted. 'Accidents do happen, and that's why there are rules about not looking through the curtains. In any case it is very unprofessional. You really are a silly girl, Georgia, and you've only yourself to blame.'

Olivia looked after them thoughtfully. She had seen Georgia careering though the curtain at high speed and it didn't look to her as if she'd slipped. It had looked very much to Olivia as if Georgia had been pushed. She wondered who had done it, and why.

By Lyn Gardner

The Many Worlds of Albie Bright

'What are you doing for your science project then?' I ask him, trying to change the subject.

Wesley scowls. 'She's got me growing cress in a cupboard – again. It's the same project I've done since Year 1. But this time I've got a plan.' He leans forward with a dangerous gleam in his eye. 'When we go on our science trip tomorrow I'm going to find out the truth about the duck-billed platypus and you're going to help me.'

I don't like the sound of this. Tomorrow Miss Benjamin is taking Class 6 on a school trip to the Clackthorpe Museum of Natural History and Mechanical Wonders. According to Kiran, this is the same school trip that the class has been on for the past five years. He says it's called a museum but that it's really just a big house filled with loads of old junk. It used to belong to a Victorian explorer called Montague Wilkes, who left Clackthorpe to explore the world and sent everything he found back home again before he carked it in the middle of Australia. I've had a look on the museum's website and most of the things he found seem to be stuffed animals. I'd even spotted what looked like a duck-billed platypus stuck in a glass jar and I now had the horrible feeling that this was part of Wesley's plan.

'Er, I don't think I'm going to be able to make it to the museum tomorrow. It was my mum's funeral yesterday–'

Nearly as fast as an atom whizzing round the Large Hadron Collider, Wesley's fist shoots out to give me a dead arm.

'Ow!'

'You'd better help me tomorrow,' Wesley warns me, 'or else. And don't think you can use your mum as an excuse. Loads of people haven't got a mum, but you won't catch me crying about it.'

By Christopher Edge

Sophie's Snail

'Wait for me,' said Sophie. But they didn't, so she plodded after them.

When she caught up with the twins in a far corner of the garden, each was examining the underside of a large snail. Sophie was not surprised to see that the snails were also obviously twins: the same size, the same shape, the same striped greeny-browny colour.

'I know!' said Matthew.

'I know what you're going to say!' said Mark.

'Let's have a snail race!' they said.

'How are you going to tell them apart?' said Sophie.

'I know!' said Mark.

'I know what you're going to say!' said Matthew.

'Fetch us a felt pen, Sophie,' they said.

'What are you going to do?' asked Sophie when she came back with a red felt pen.

'Put my initial on my snail,' said Mark and Matthew together.

'But you've got the same initial.'

The boys looked at each other.

'I know!' they said.

'I know what you're going to say,' said Sophie, and she plodded off again. She came back with a blue felt pen. After a moment, 'Ready?' said Matthew, holding up his snail with a big red M on its shell, and at the same instant, 'Ready?' said Mark, holding up his snail with a big blue M.

'Wait for me,' said Sophie. 'I haven't got a snail yet.' But already the twins had set their snails side by side on the path that ran between the edge of the lawn and the flowerbed.

By Dick King-Smith

Five Go Adventuring Again

The four children crept downstairs through the dark and silent night. Nobody made a sound at all. They made their way to the study. George softly closed the door and then switched on the light.

The children stared at the eight panels over the mantelpiece. Yes – there were exactly eight, four in one row and four in the row above. Julian spread the linen roll out on the table, and the children pored over it.

'The cross is in the middle of the second panel in the top row,' said Julian in a low voice. 'I'll try pressing it. Watch, all of you!'

He went to the fireplace. The others followed him, their hearts beating fast with excitement. Julian stood on tiptoe and began to press hard in the middle of the second panel. Nothing happened.

'Press harder! Tap it!' said Dick.

'I daren't make too much noise,' said Julian, feeling all over the panel to see if there was any roughness that might tell of a hidden spring or lever.

Suddenly, under his hands, the panel slid silently back, just as the one had done at Kirrin Farmhouse in the hall! The children stared at the space behind, thrilled.

'It's not big enough to get into,' said George. 'It can't be the entrance to the Secret Way.'

Julian got out his torch from his dressing-gown pocket. He put it inside the opening, and gave a low exclamation.

'There's a sort of handle here – with strong wire or something attached to it. I'll pull it and see what happens.'

By Enid Blyton

Arsenic for Tea

We crept out onto the landing. It was empty. My heart was beating fast – I couldn't quite believe that we were about to break into Miss Alston's little box room. What if she came up and found us?

The door was shut. Daisy went tiptoeing up to it, twisted the handle and carefully pushed it open.

It felt most dreadfully wrong. Miss Alston was such a secretive person – we really knew nothing about her at all. I had never even seen inside her bedroom, and nor had any of the others. I imagined her doorway as an invisible line that, if crossed, would burn you up into a crisp or freeze you to death.

'Oh no!' whispered Beanie as Daisy poked a careful shoe-tip through the doorway, then craned her neck round, and I could tell that she felt as uncomfortable as I did.

'What, Beanie?' said Daisy, without turning her head.

'I don't think this is legal!' whispered Beanie nervously.

'Of *course* it's not legal, Beanie. But we're detecting so that makes things all right.'

'I don't want to go in!' Beanie's face crumpled.

'All right then, stay out here! No one's making you. You can be our lookout. If Miss Alston comes up the stairs, whistle, or squeak, or something. Hazel, Kitty, are you coming?

With Beanie trembling on the landing, we had to. Shooting nervous glances at each other, Kitty and I crept forward, and over the dividing line into Miss Alston's bedroom. I did not burn up – although I did feel a rush of shame that made me tingle with heat all the way to the tips of my fingers.

Inside, everything was neatly ordered – drawers shut, bed made with military precision, and a gleaming row of schoolbooks laid out in alphabetical order. It was so neat that I was terrified all over again. What if we left signs of our presence? If she was not the murderer, she would be furious. And if she was…I shivered.

By Robin Stevens

Black Beauty

As we came back through the park we met the Squire and Mrs. Gordon walking; they stopped, and John jumped off.

"Well, John, how does he go?"

"First-rate, sir," answered John; "he is as fleet as a deer, and has a fine spirit too; but the lightest touch of the rein will guide him. Down at the end of the common we met one of those traveling carts hung all over with baskets, rugs, and such like; you know, sir, many horses will not pass those carts quietly; he just took a good look at it, and then went on as quiet and pleasant as could be. They were shooting rabbits near the Highwood, and a gun went off close by; he pulled up a little and looked, but did not stir a step to right or left. I just held the rein steady and did not hurry him, and it's my opinion he has not been frightened or ill-used while he was young."

"That's well," said the squire, "I will try him myself to-morrow." The next day I was brought up for my master. I remembered my mother's counsel and my good old master's, and I tried to do exactly what he wanted me to do. I found he was a very good rider, and thoughtful for his horse too. When he came home the lady was at the hall door as he rode up.

"Well, my dear," she said, "how do you like him?"

"He is exactly what John said," he replied; "a pleasanter creature I never wish to mount. What shall we call him?"

"Would you like Ebony?" said she; "he is as black as ebony."

"No, not Ebony."

"Will you call him Blackbird, like your uncle's old horse?"

"No, he is far handsomer than old Blackbird ever was."

"Yes," she said, "he is really quite a beauty, and he has such a sweet, good-tempered face, and such a fine, intelligent eye—what do you say to calling him Black Beauty?"

"Black Beauty—why, yes, I think that is a very good name. If you like it shall be his name;" and so it was.

By Anna Sewell

Level 1 Speaking Verse and Prose:

Grade 3 – Verse

Titles in Level 1 Speaking Verse and Prose:
Grade 3 – Verse

Truth

Sticks and stones may break my bones
but words can also hurt me.
Stones and sticks break only skin,
while words are ghosts that haunt me.

Slant and curved the word-swords fall
to pierce and stick inside me.
Bats and bricks may ache through bones
but words can mortify me.

Pain from words has left its scar
on mind and heart that's tender.
Cuts and bruises now have healed;
it's words that I remember.

By Barrie Wade

Extract from The Bed Book

Beds come in all sizes –
Single or double,
Cot-size or cradle,
King-size or trundle.

Most Beds are Beds
For sleeping or resting,
But the *best* Beds are much
More interesting!

Not just a white little
Tucked-in-tight little
Nighty-night little
Turn-out-the-light little
Bed –

Instead
A Bed for Fishing,
A Bed for Cats,
A Bed for a Troupe of
Acrobats.

The *right* sort of Bed
(If you see what I mean)
Is a Bed that might
Be a submarine

Nosing through water

Clear and green,

Silver and glittery

As a sardine

Or a Jet-Propelled Bed

For visiting Mars

With mosquito nets

For the shooting stars...

By Sylvia Plath

People Ask

My father travelled from Ceylon
Island of cinnamon and rubies
To my mother's birthplace
In the heart of Yorkshire

People ask
Where do you come from?
I say:
From more places
Than you imagine
My father's memories
My mother's dreams
Mines of gems and coal
Mango sunsets over rhubarb fields

People ask
Which half of you is white?
I say:
There are no halves in me
Everything is whole
I am a myriad of mingling
Multicoloured stories
Whispering wisely down
Through centuries

People ask

Where do you belong?

I say:

In the world

In my father's hopes

In my mother's songs

Most of all

In the place inside myself

Shining with its own futures

By Seni Seneviratne

The Jade Staircase

The jade staircase is bright with dew.

Slowly, this long night, the queen climbs,
Letting her gauze stockings and her elaborate robe
Drag in the shining water.

Dazed with the light,
She lowers the crystal blind
Before the door of the pavilion.

It leaps down like a waterfall in sunlight.

While the tiny clashing dies down,
Sad and long dreaming,
She watches between the fragments of jade light
The shining of the autumn moon.

By Li Po
Translated by Edward Powys Mathers

Do Not Stand at My Grave and Weep

Do not stand at my grave and weep

I am not there. I do not sleep.

I am a thousand winds that blow.

I am the diamond glints on snow.

I am the sunlight on ripened grain.

I am the gentle autumn rain.

When you awaken in the morning's hush

I am the swift uplifting rush

Of quiet birds in circled flight.

I am the soft stars that shine at night.

Do not stand at my grave and cry;

I am not there. I did not die.

By Mary Elizabeth Frye

The Travellers and the Purse

Two friends once were walking in sociable chat,
When a purse one espied on the ground;
'Oh, see!' said he, (thank my fortune for that,)
'What a large sum of money I've found!'

'Nay, do not say *I*' said his friend, 'for you know
'Tis but friendship to share it with me;'
'I share it with you,' said the other. 'How so?
He who *found* it the owner should be.'

'Be it so,' said his friend, 'but what sound do I hear?
'Stop thief!' one is calling to you;
He comes with a constable close in the rear!'
Said the other, 'Oh, what shall we do?'

'Nay, do not say *we*,' said his friend, 'for you know
You claimed the sole right to the prize!
And since all the money was taken by you,
With you the dishonesty lies.'

By Marmaduke Park

Beachcomber

Monday I found a boot –
Rust and salt leather.
I gave it back to the sea, to dance in.

Tuesday a spar of timber worth thirty bob.
Next winter
It will be a chair, a coffin, a bed.

Wednesday a half can of Swedish spirits.
I tilted my head.
The shore was cold with mermaids and angels.

Thursday I got nothing, seaweed,
A whale bone,
Wet feet and a loud cough.

Friday I held a seaman's skull,
Sand spilling from it
The way time is told on kirkyard stones.

Saturday a barrel of sodden oranges.
A Spanish ship
Was wrecked last month at The Kame.

Sunday, for fear of the elders,
I sit on my bum.
What's heaven? A sea chest with a thousand gold coins.

By George Mackay Brown

It Couldn't Be Done

Somebody said that it couldn't be done,

But he with a chuckle replied

That 'maybe it couldn't,' but he would be one

Who wouldn't say so till he'd tried.

So he buckled right in with the trace of a grin

On his face. If he worried he hid it.

He started to sing as he tackled the thing

That couldn't be done, and he did it!

Somebody scoffed: 'Oh, you'll never do that;

At least no one ever has done it;'

But he took off his coat and he took off his hat,

And the first thing we knew he'd begun it.

With a lift of his chin and a bit of a grin,

Without any doubting or quiddit,

He started to sing as he tackled the thing

That couldn't be done, and he did it.

There are thousands to tell you it cannot be done,

There are thousands to prophesy failure,

There are thousands to point out to you one by one,

The dangers that wait to assail you.

But just buckle in with a bit of a grin,

Just take off your coat and go to it;

Just start in to sing as you tackle the thing

That 'cannot be done,' and you'll do it.

By Edgar A. Guest

Level 1 Speaking Verse and Prose:

Grade 3 – Prose

Titles in Level 1 Speaking Verse and Prose:
Grade 3 – Prose

White Boots

Letters from the Lighthouse

The Curious Book of Birds

The Girl of Ink & Stars

Moonlocket

Moni the Goat-Boy

Noah Barleywater Runs Away

The Travels of Tom Thumb

White Boots

It was awful for Lalla going home after her test. Miss Goldthorpe tried to talk about other things, but nobody answered; Harriet kept looking at Lalla's face, and answers to Miss Goldthorpe dried up inside her mouth. She was sure, if it had been her who had hoped to pass and had failed, she would have cried, but Lalla did not look a bit like crying, she looked much more as if she might bite somebody. Her face was pink, her lips pressed together tight, and she had a very angry look in her eyes. Just before the car reached the house Lalla, still speaking in a proud voice, said:

'No one is going to tell Aunt Claudia instead of me. I know I ought to have passed it, it was those silly old judges who were wrong.'

Miss Goldthorpe looked worried. Too often in the past she had heard girls blaming the examiners when they did not pass examinations, but she did not say so. It was not the moment to make Lalla feel worse than she was feeling already. Instead she said that of course Lalla must tell Aunt Claudia, and explain that Max Lindblom had said she would try again in autumn. She and Harriet would go straight up to the schoolroom and Lalla would find Wilson and ask when her aunt would be in.

By Noel Streatfeild

Letters from the Lighthouse

'Are you from London?' a freckle faced girl asked me.

I nodded. Smiled.

'My dad says never mind the Germans, it's them Londoners what's invaded us,' an older boy remarked.

I hoped he might be joking: he certainly had a big grin on his face. Then his mate joined in with 'Send 'em all home. We don't want 'em here.'

And I realised then it wasn't a pleasant grin. Reaching for Cliff's hand, I thought it best to move on into the playground where I could see Mr Barrowman talking to Miss Carter. Glancing behind, I saw the grinning boy's new target was Esther Jenkins, who, like the rest of us, was wearing the uniform of her London school.

'Been frightening the cows in that outfit, have you?' the boy called out.

Esther stopped level with the Budmouth kids. 'Which one of you said that?'

I couldn't help but admire her courage. I'd not seen her since we'd left Queenie's on Friday, and still felt I'd behaved rather shoddily, especially now I knew a bit more about her background. I'd decided to try harder at being friendly next time we met. Watching her now, though, she still seemed full of fight, I wasn't confident my plan would work.

'Are you talking to me?' Esther asked, homing in on the boy with the grin. 'We're guests here, you know. Is *this* how you welcome us?'

Chin up, plaits tossed over her shoulders, she more than stood her ground. The boy, on the other hand, had gone decidedly blotchy.

'That ain't a London accent,' he laughed nervously. 'You sound foreign, you do.'

I caught my breath. There was going to be trouble. I could see Esther's fists clenching by her sides.

Thankfully, Mr Barrowman started ringing the school bell with a huge swing of his arm. Deafening though it was, the noise broke up the group.

By Emma Carroll

The Curious Book of Birds

Now the Eagle expected to be king. He felt sure that he could fly higher than anyone else. He sat apart on a tall pine tree, looking very dignified and noble, as a future king should look. And the birds glanced at one another, nodded their heads, and whispered, 'He is sure to be elected king. He can fly straight up toward the sun without winking, and his great wings are so strong, so strong! He never grows tired. He is sure to be king.'

Thus they whispered among themselves, and the Eagle heard them, and was pleased. But the little brown Wren heard also, and he was not pleased. The absurd little bird! He wanted to be king himself, although he was one of the tiniest birds there, who could never be a protector to the others, nor stop trouble when it began. No, indeed! Fancy him stepping as a peacemaker between a robber Hawk and a Falcon. It was they who would make pieces of him. But he was a conceited little creature, and saw no reason why he should not make a noble sovereign.

'I am cleverer than the Eagle,' he said to himself, 'though he is so much bigger. I will be king in spite of him. Ha-ha! We shall see what we shall see!' For the Wren had a great idea in his wee little head—an idea bigger than the head itself, if you can explain how that could be. He ruffled up his feathers to make himself as huge as possible, and hopped over to the branch where the Eagle was sitting.

'Well, Eagle,' said the Wren pompously, 'I suppose you expect to be king, eh?'

The Eagle stared hard at him with his great bright eyes. 'Well, if I do, what of that?' he said. 'Who will dispute me?'

'I shall,' said the Wren, bobbing his little brown head and wriggling his tail saucily.

'You!' said the Eagle. 'Do *you* expect to fly higher than I?'

'Yes,' chirped the Wren, 'I do. Yes, I do, do, do!'

By Abbie Farwell Brown

The Girl of Ink & Stars

'Isabella, look!'

I blinked blearily into the midday glare. 'What is it?'

I felt suddenly awake. Ahead, the ground seemed to drop away into nothing. Except I knew it was not nothing – it was Arintan. We were coming to the edge of the ridge the expedition had followed on its outward journey.

Pablo set me down, steadying me as the blood prickled back into my legs. 'Nearly home,' he said.

I walked to the edge of the waterfall and peered over. 'It's a long drop.'

Lupe looked too, then passed Miss La to me and without pausing scrambled halfway down the rocks. She tucked her skirts up and jumped lightly down, landing with a quiet splash. I gaped at her as she climbed back up simple as a cat, barely panting. 'Not so bad.'

'Show off,' mumbled Pablo.

It was as I turned to tell him that I felt it: the pushing away, my insides twisting. Pablo's face creased and he held his stomach. 'What is that?'

'Oh, no,' said Lupe frantically. 'Oh, no, no, no!'

'Run!' I shouted, just as a huge shape materialized behind Pablo.

But there was no time. Pablo turned to see the Tibicena, its hackles raised along its spine, the slash of its mouth opening in a booming roar, like a thousand rocks smashing down a cliff.

'Help me!' I yelled, heaving at a boulder by the waterfall's edge.

By Kiran Millwood Hargrave

Moonlocket

'Where are we, boy?' the man whispered, suddenly close by his side. He had woken and Robert hadn't even heard or noticed him move!

'We fell through the floor.' Robert tried to keep his voice from shaking and muster some bravery from the slush inside. 'We're in a locked room. Lily's gone for help.'

'Lily is it?' the man purred.

'It. Is.' Robert spat the words like bullets, but inwardly he cursed himself for giving her name away. 'And when she gets back with the police you'll be done for trespass. Then we'll see what's what.'

The man gave a hearty laugh that set Robert's teeth on edge. 'But I won't be here, boy.' He leaned in close until Robert could feel the man's breath against his face.

'You still don't know who I am, do you?'

'N-no.' Robert shook his head, then watched in horror as the man ran a finger down his scarred cheek.

'Need a clue? Ah, you'll know soon enough.' The man stepped away to the ill-lit far corner of the small room and Robert heard him rattle the door handle.

'You won't open that before they return,' he said, with more confidence than he felt. 'Thaddeus Townsend built that lock and it's fail–'

'–safe,' the man finished for him. 'You're talking to someone who's cracked them all, lad! Let's have some light shall we?' He struck a match and the flame illuminated his grin as he held it up to the lock for a second. Then it went out.

'What are you doing here?' Robert asked.

'Looking for something that belongs to me.' The man grunted. 'Something stolen,' he hissed under his breath. 'But I'll catch up with that traitor Selena. She'll regret the day she ever crossed me.'

Robert felt a wave of shock. The man was talking about his ma!

By Peter Bunzl

Moni the Goat-Boy

Now he heard a faint, pitiful bleating; it was Mäggerli's voice, and it came from below so plaintive and beseeching. Moni lay down on the ground and leaned over. There below something was moving; now he saw quite plainly, far down Mäggerli was hanging to the bough of a tree which grew out of the rock, and was moaning pitifully; she must have fallen over.

Fortunately the bough had caught her, otherwise she would have fallen into the ravine and met a sorry death. Even now if she could no longer hold to the bough, she would fall into the depths and be dashed to pieces.

In the greatest anguish he called down: "Hold fast, Mäggerli, hold fast to the bough! See, I am coming to get you!" But how could he reach there? The wall of rock was so steep here, Moni saw very well that it would be impossible to go down that way. But the little goat must be down there somewhere near the Rain-rock, the overhanging stone under which good protection was to be found in rainy weather; the goat-boys had always spent rainy days there, therefore the stone had been called from old times the Rain-rock. From there, Moni thought he could climb across over the rocks and so bring back the little kid.

He quickly whistled the flock together and went with them down to the place from which he could reach the Rain-rock. There he left them to graze and went to the rock. Here he immediately saw, just a little bit above him, the bough of the tree, and the kid hanging to it. He saw very well that it would not be an easy task to climb up there and then down again with Mäggerli on his back, but there was no other way to rescue her. He also thought the dear Lord would surely stand by him, and then he could not possibly fail. He folded his hands, looked up to heaven and prayed: "Oh, dear Lord, help me, so that I can save Mäggerli!"

By Johanna Spyri

Noah Barleywater Runs Away

He turned round and glanced back towards the entrance of the shop but – and this was a great surprise – he couldn't see the door any more. He must have wandered so far in that it was no longer possible. Only he couldn't remember walking that far at all, and the shop hadn't even seemed particularly big at first, certainly not big enough to lose yourself in. In fact, when he looked back, he couldn't see any way in or out of the shop, and no sign pointing towards the exit. All that stood behind him was hundreds and hundreds of wooden puppets, each one staring defiantly at him, smiling, laughing, frowning, threatening. Every emotion he could think of, good and bad. Every sensation. Suddenly he felt as if these puppets were not his friends at all and were moving, one by one, in his direction, surrounding him, trapping him inside an ever-decreasing circle.

'Who is he anyway?' they were whispering.

'A stranger.'

'We don't like strangers.'

'Kind of funny-looking too, isn't he?'

'Short for his age.'

'Mightn't have had his growth spurt yet.'

'Nice hair though.'

The voices grew more and more numerous, although they never rose above a whisper, and soon he couldn't make out any of the words at all, as they were all speaking at the same time and jumbling them up together into a language he didn't understand. They were closing in on him now, and he held his hands up in fright, closed his eyes, spun round and counted to three, thinking that none of this could possibly be happening and that when he took his hands away and opened his eyes again, he better just scream as loudly as he could and then surely someone would come and rescue him.

One,

Two,

Three–

'Hello,' said a man's voice then, the only voice to be heard now, for the chorus of puppets had become immediately silent. 'And who might you be?'

By John Boyne

The Travels of Tom Thumb

As soon as they saw the little tailor, they said to themselves, 'A little fellow like this could creep through a keyhole, and aid us greatly.' So one called out–

'Hullo, little man, will you come with us to the king's treasury? Certainly a Goliath like you could creep in with ease, and throw out the coins to us.'

After considering awhile, Tom Thumb consented, and accompanied them to the king's treasury.

From top to bottom they inspected the door to discover a crack large enough for him to get through, and soon found one. He was for going in directly, but one of the sentinels happening to catch sight of him, exclaimed: 'Here is indeed an ugly spider; I will crush it with my foot.'

'Leave the poor creature alone,' the other said; 'it has not done you any harm.'

So Tom Thumb slipped through the crack, and made his way to the treasury. Then he opened the window, and cast out the coins to the robbers who were waiting below. While the little tailor was engaged in this exciting employment, he heard the king coming to inspect his treasure, so as quickly as possible he crept out of sight. The king noticed that his treasure had been disarranged, and soon observed that coins were missing: but he was utterly unable to think how they could have been stolen, for the locks and bolts had not been tampered with, and everything was well fastened.

Ongoing from the treasury, he warned the two sentinels, saying–

'Be on the watch, someone is after the money,' and quite soon, on Tom Thumb setting to work again, they heard very clearly the coins ringing, chink, chank, as they struck one against the other.

As quickly as possible they unfastened the building and went in, hoping to take the thief.

But Tom Thumb was too quick for them, he sprang into a corner, and hiding himself behind a coin, so that nothing of him was visible, he made fun of the sentinels; crying 'I am here!' Then when the men hurried to the spot where the voice came from, he was no longer there, but from a different place cried out: 'Ha, Ha! here I am!'

By Jacob and Wilhelm Grimm

113

Level 2 Speaking Verse and Prose:
Grade 4 – Verse

Titles in Level 2 Speaking Verse and Prose:
Grade 4 – Verse

The Kitten in the Falling Snow

The year-old kitten
has never seen snow,
fallen or falling, until now
this late winter afternoon.

He sits with wide eyes
at the firelit window, sees
white things falling
from black trees.

Are they petals, leaves or birds?
they cannot be the cabbage whites
he battered briefly with his paws,
or the puffball seeds in summer grass.

They make no sound, they have no wings
and yet they can whirl and fly around
until they swoop like swallows, and
disappear into the ground.

'Where do they go?' he questions,
with eyes ablaze, following their flight
into black stone. So I put him
out into the yard, to make their acquaintance.

He has to look up at them: when one

blanches his coral nose, he sneezes,

and flicks a few from his whiskers, from

his sharpened ear, that picks up silences.

He catches one on a curled-up paw

and licks it quickly, before

its strange milk fades, then sniffs its ghost,

a wetness, while his black coat

shivers with stars of flickering frost.

He shivers at something else that makes his thin

tail swish, his fur stand on end! 'What's this?…'

Then he suddenly scoots in to safety

and sits again with wide eyes

at the firelit window, sees

white things falling

from black trees.

By James Kirkup

Encounter

We were riding through frozen fields in a wagon at dawn.
A red wing rose in the darkness.

And suddenly a hare ran across the road.
One of us pointed to it with his hand.

That was long ago. Today neither of them is alive,
Not the hare, nor the man who made the gesture.

O my love, where are they, where are they going
The flash of a hand, streak of movement, rustle of pebbles.
I ask not out of sorrow, but in wonder.

By Czeslaw Milosz
Translated by Czeslaw Milosz and Lillian Vallee

Barter

Life has loveliness to sell,
All beautiful and splendid things,
Blue waves whitened on a cliff,
Soaring fire that sways and sings,
And children's faces looking up
Holding wonder like a cup.
Life has loveliness to sell,
Music like a curve of gold,
Scent of pine trees in the rain,
Eyes that love you, arms that hold,
And for your spirit's still delight,
Holy thoughts that star the night.
Spend all you have for loveliness,
Buy it and never count the cost;
For one white singing hour of peace
Count many a year of strife well lost,
And for a breath of ecstasy
Give all you have been, or could be.

By Sara Teasdale

The Disappointed

There are songs enough for the hero
Who dwells on the heights of fame;
I sing for the disappointed—
For those who missed their aim.

I sing with a tearful cadence
For one who stands in the dark,
And knows that his last, best arrow
Has bounded back from the mark.

I sing for the breathless runner,
The eager, anxious soul,
Who falls with his strength exhausted,
Almost in sight of the goal;

For the hearts that break in silence,
With a sorrow all unknown,
For those who need companions,
Yet walk their ways alone.

There are songs enough for the lovers
Who share love's tender pain,
I sing for the one whose passion
Is given all in vain.

For those whose spirit comrades
Have missed them on the way,
I sing, with a heart o'erflowing,
This minor strain to-day.

And I know the Solar system
Must somewhere keep in space

A prize for that spent runner

Who barely lost the race.

For the plan would be imperfect

Unless it held some sphere

That paid for the toil and talent

And love that are wasted here.

By Ella Wheeler Wilcox

Empty House

I hate our house when there's no one in

I miss my family and I miss the din.

The rooms and the hallway seem cold and bare

And the silence hangs like dust in the air.

What's that sound upstairs that makes me start

Driving Fear like an icicle through my heart?

I'm imagining things, there's nobody there –

But I have to make sure so I creep up the stair.

I stand holding my breath by the bedroom door

And hear something rustling across the floor.

Then a scratching sound, a tiny cry!

I can't seem to breathe, my throat is dry.

In the silence I hear my own heart beating

And the rumble of water in the central heating.

I should go in but I just don't dare

So I call aloud, 'Is anyone there?'

Nobody answers. I push open the door.

A fluttering shadow crosses the floor.

And now I see him, now understand

And I gather him gently in my hands.

'I won't hurt you, my friend. Don't flutter, don't start.'

But his body beats wild like a feathered heart.

Out through the window, watch him wheel and fly

Carrying my fear across the sky.

By Gareth Owen

Playthings

Child, how happy you are sitting in the dust, playing with a broken twig all the morning.

I smile at your play with that little bit of a broken twig.

I am busy with my accounts, adding up figures by the hour.

Perhaps you glance at me and think, 'What a stupid game to spoil your morning with!'

Child, I have forgotten the art of being absorbed in sticks and mud-pies.

I seek out costly playthings, and gather lumps of gold and silver.

With whatever you find you create your glad games, I spend both my time and my strength over things I never can obtain.

In my frail canoe I struggle to cross the sea of desire, and forget that I too am playing a game.

By Rabindranath Tagore

Herbert Glerbett

Herbert Glerbett, rather round,

swallowed sherbet by the pound,

fifty pounds of lemon sherbet

went inside of Herbert Glerbett.

With that glob inside his lap

Herbert Glerbett took a nap,

and as he slept, the boy dissolved,

and from the mess a thing evolved–

a thing that is a ghastly green,

a thing the world had never seen,

a puddle thing, a gooey pile

of something strange that does not smile.

Now if you're wise, and if you're sly,

you'll swiftly pass this creature by,

it is no longer Herbert Glerbett.

Whatever it is, do not disturb it.

By Jack Prelutsky

I Ask My Mother to Sing

She begins, and my grandmother joins her.
Mother and daughter sing like young girls.
If my father were alive, he would play
his accordion and sway like a boat.

I've never been in Peking, or the Summer Palace,
nor stood on the great Stone Boat to watch
the rain begin on Kuen Ming Lake, the picnickers
running away in the grass.

But I love to hear it sung;
how the waterlilies fill with rain until
they overturn, spilling water into water,
then rock back, and fill with more.

Both women have begun to cry.
But neither stops her song.

By Li-Young Lee

Level 2 Speaking Verse and Prose:

Grade 4 – Prose

Titles in Level 2 Speaking Verse and Prose:
Grade 4 – Prose

Rooftoppers

Neverwhere

The Garden Party and other stories

The Curious Incident of the Dog in the Night-Time

Harry Potter and the Deathly Hallows

The Diary of a Nobody

The Extinction Trials

The ABC Murders

Rooftoppers

If she had obeyed Charles and stayed in her room all day and all night, Sophie would, she thought, have gone straightforwardly crazy. She tried to reassure herself that she was not breaking any rules. She was not opening the door to her bedroom. The thought of the rooftops kept her steady during the day. Sophie counted the hours until sunset.

By nightfall it had grown cold, and Sophie put on her two pairs of stockings under her nightdress. She hadn't packed enough warm clothes, so she pulled the pillowcases off the pillows and knotted them together to make a scarf. It felt limp and not entirely comfortable, but she thought it was preferable to nothing. Then she got into bed, and wedged her hairbrush behind her neck so she wouldn't fall asleep, and waited.

Matteo arrived as the clocks struck the half hour. He knocked on the skylight, and then stood impatiently flicking pebbles down into her room until she climbed out.

'Hello,' said Sophie. '*Bonsoir.*'

'*Oui bonsoir.*' He wore a pack on his back, and his shorts had been swapped for a pair of trousers. They looked like they had been in a fight, and lost. He said, 'You're learning French?'

'A little.' Sophie flushed. 'It's not easy.'

'Yes it is. I know dogs that speak French. I know *pigeons*.'

'That's different.'

'How? How is it different?'

'Well, I'm not a pigeon.' A thought struck her. 'How long did it take you to learn English? Do all French people speak it like you do?'

'*Je ne sais pas.* I always knew it, a little. There's a bar where the English diplomats go. It has a courtyard. I can hear them speaking from my rooftop. And I learnt to read it while I was in–' He stopped.

'While you were where?'

'In an orphanage.'

By Katherine Rundell

127

Neverwhere

'Oy,' hissed the man. Richard looked back at him. He was beckoning. 'Come on, down here, quickly man.' The man hurried down some steps on the derelict houses at the side of the road – rubbish-strewn steps, leading down to abandoned basement flats, and Richard stumbled after him. At the bottom of the steps was a door, which the man pushed open. He waited for Richard to go through, and shut the door behind them. Through the door, they were in darkness. There was a scratch, and the noise of a match flaring into life: the man touched the match to the wick of an old railwayman's lamp, which caught, casting slightly less light than the match had, and they walked together through a dark place.

It smelled musty, of damp and old brick, of rot and the dark. 'Where are we?' Richard whispered. His guide shushed him to silence. They reached another door set in a wall. The man rapped on it rhythmically. There was a pause, and then the door swung open.

For a moment, Richard was blinded by the sudden light. He was standing in a huge, vaulted room, an underground hall, filled with firelight and smoke. Small fires burned around the room. Shadowy people stood by the flames, roasting small animals on spits. People scurried from fire to fire. It reminded him of Hell, or rather, the way that he had thought of Hell, as a schoolboy. The smoke scraped his chest, and he coughed. A hundred eyes turned, then, and stared at him: a hundred eyes, unblinking and unfriendly.

A man scuttled towards them. He had long hair, a patchy brown beard, and his ragged clothes were trimmed with fur – orange-and-white-and-black fur, like the coat of a tortoiseshell cat. He would have been taller than Richard, but he walked with a pronounced stoop, his hands held up at his chest, fingers pressed together. 'What? What is it? What is this?' he asked Richard's guide. 'Who've you bought us, Iliaster? Talk-talk-talk.'

'He's from the Upside,' said the guide.

By Neil Gaiman

The Garden Party and other stories

A few moments later the back door of one of the bungalows opened, and a figure in a broad-striped bathing suit flung down the paddock, cleared the stile, rushed through the tussock grass into the hollow, staggered up the sandy hillock, and raced for dear life over the big porous stones, over the cold, wet pebbles, on to the hard sand that gleamed like oil. Splish-Splosh! Splish-Splosh! The water bubbled round his legs as Stanley Burnell waded out exulting. First man in as usual! He'd beaten them all again. And he swooped down to souse his head and neck.

"Hail, brother! All hail, Thou Mighty One!" A velvety bass voice came booming over the water.

Great Scott! Damnation take it! Stanley lifted up to see a dark head bobbing far out and an arm lifted. It was Jonathan Trout— there before him! "Glorious morning!" sang the voice.

"Yes, very fine!" said Stanley briefly. Why the dickens didn't the fellow stick to his part of the sea? Why should he come barging over to this exact spot? Stanley gave a kick, a lunge and struck out, swimming overarm. But Jonathan was a match for him. Up he came, his black hair sleek on his forehead, his short beard sleek.

"I had an extraordinary dream last night!" he shouted.

What was the matter with the man? This mania for conversation irritated Stanley beyond words. And it was always the same— always some piffle about a dream he'd had, or some cranky idea he'd got hold of, or some rot he'd been reading. Stanley turned over on his back and kicked with his legs till he was a living waterspout. But even then.... "I dreamed I was hanging over a terrifically high cliff, shouting to someone below." You would be! thought Stanley. He could stick no more of it. He stopped splashing. "Look here, Trout," he said, "I'm in rather a hurry this morning."

"You're WHAT?" Jonathan was so surprised—or pretended to be— that he sank under the water, then reappeared again blowing.

"All I mean is," said Stanley, "I've no time to—to—to fool about. I want to get this over. I'm in a hurry. I've work to do this morning— see?"

Jonathan was gone before Stanley had finished. "Pass, friend!" said the bass voice gently, and he slid away through the water with scarcely a ripple.... But curse the fellow! He'd ruined Stanley's bathe. What an unpractical idiot the man was! Stanley struck out to sea again, and then as quickly swam in again, and away he rushed up the beach. He felt cheated.

By Katherine Mansfield

The Curious Incident of the Dog in the Night-Time

Father's eyes were still closed. I wondered if he was pretending to be asleep. So I gripped the penknife really hard and I knocked on the doorframe.

Father moved his head from one side to the other and his foot twitched and he said 'Gnnnn,' but his eyes stayed closed. And then he snored again.

He was asleep.

That meant I could get out of the house if I was really quiet so I didn't wake him up.

I took both my coats and my scarf from the hooks next to the front door and I put them all on because it would be cold outside at night. Then I went upstairs again really quietly, but it was difficult because my legs were shaking. I went into my room and I picked up Toby's cage. He was making scratching noises, so I took off one of the coats and put it over the cage to make the noise quieter. Then I carried him downstairs again.

Father was still asleep.

I went into the kitchen and I picked up my special food box. I unlocked the back door and stepped outside. Then I held the handle of the door down as I shut it again so that the click wasn't too loud. Then I walked down to the bottom of the garden.

At the bottom of the garden is a shed. It has the lawnmower and the hedge cutter in, and lots of gardening equipment that mother used to use, like pots and bags of compost and bamboo canes and string and spades. It would be a bit warmer in the shed but I knew that Father might look for me in the shed, so I went round the back of the shed and I squeezed into the gap between the wall of the shed and the fence, behind the big, black, plastic tub for collecting rainwater. Then I sat down and I felt a bit safer.

I decided to leave my other coat over Toby's cage because I didn't want him to get cold and die.

I opened up my special food box. Inside was the Milky Bar and two liquorice laces and three clementines and a pink wafer biscuit and my red food colouring. I didn't feel hungry but I knew that I should eat something because if you don't eat something you can get cold, so I ate two clementines and the Milky Bar.

Then I wondered what I would do next.

By Mark Haddon

Harry Potter and the Deathly Hallows

'I thought there was a Ministry of Magic?' asked Vernon Dursley abruptly.

'There is,' said Harry, surprised.

'Well, then, why can't they protect us? It seems to me that, as innocent victims, guilty of nothing more than harbouring a marked man, we ought to qualify for government protection!'

Harry laughed; he could not stop himself. It was so typical of his uncle to put his hopes in the establishment, even within this world that he despised and mistrusted.

'You heard what Mr. Weasley and Kingsley said,' Harry replied. 'We think the Ministry has been infiltrated.'

Uncle Vernon strode to the fireplace and back, breathing so heavily that his great black moustache rippled, his face still purple with concentration.

'All right,' he said, stopping in front of Harry yet again. 'All right, let's say, for the sake of argument, we accept this protection. I still don't see why we can't have that Kingsley bloke.'

Harry managed not to roll his eyes, but with difficulty. This question had also been addressed half a dozen times. 'As I've told you,' he said, through gritted teeth. 'Kingsley is protecting the Mug – I mean, your Prime Minister.'

'Exactly – he's the best!' said Uncle Vernon, pointing at the blank television screen. The Dursleys had spotted Kingsley on the news, walking along discreetly behind the Muggle Prime Minister as he visited a hospital. This, and the fact that Kingsley had mastered the knack of dressing like a Muggle, not to mention a certain reassuring something in his slow, deep voice, had caused the Dursleys to take to Kingsley in a way that they had certainly not done with any other wizard, although it was true that they had never seen him with his earring in.

'Well, he's taken,' said Harry. 'But Hestia Jones and Dedalus Diggle are more than up to the job – '

'If we'd even seen CVs . . .' began Uncle Vernon, but Harry lost patience. Getting to his feet, he advanced on his uncle, now pointing at the TV set himself.

'These accidents aren't accidents – the crashes and explosions and derailments and whatever else has happened since we last watched the news. People are disappearing and dying and he's behind it – Voldemort. I've told you this over and over again, he kills Muggles for fun. Even the fogs – they're caused by Dementors, and if you can't remember what they are, ask your son!'

By J. K. Rowling

The Diary of a Nobody

April 9.–Commenced the morning badly. The butcher, whom we decided not to arrange with, called and blackguarded me in the most uncalled-for manner. He began by abusing me, and saying he did not want my custom. I simply said: 'Then what are you making all this fuss about it for?' And he shouted out at the top of his voice, so that all the neighbours could hear: 'Pah! go along. Ugh! I could buy up 'things' like you by the dozen!'

I shut the door, and was giving Carrie to understand that this disgraceful scene was entirely her fault, when there was a violent kicking at the door, enough to break the panels. It was the blackguard butcher again, who said he had cut his foot over the scraper, and would immediately bring an action against me. Called at Farmerson's, the ironmonger, on my way to town, and gave him the job of moving the scraper and repairing the bells, thinking it scarcely worth while to trouble the landlord with such a trifling matter.

Arrived home tired and worried. Mr. Putley, a painter and decorator, who had sent in a card, said he could not match the colour on the stairs, as it contained Indian carmine. He said he spent half-a-day calling at warehouses to see if he could get it. He suggested he should entirely repaint the stairs. It would cost very little more; if he tried to match it, he could only make a bad job of it. It would be more satisfactory to him and to us to have the work done properly. I consented, but felt I had been talked over. Planted some mustard-and-cress and radishes, and went to bed at nine.

By George and Weedon Grossmith

The Extinction Trials

'What are you talking about, Storm? You can't possibly want to go to Piloria? It's a death sentence. Everyone knows that.' There was panic in his voice.

'But what if it isn't?' The volume of her voice was increasing. 'What if it means we get to hang on to that feeling? What if it's a chance?'

'It's a chance to get eaten by dinosaurs!'

She flung up her hands in obvious frustration. 'What if it's a chance to experience something completely different? No grey buildings. No work regimes. No school. How do we really know what the dinosaurs are like? Maybe they're not all horrible people-eating monsters, maybe some of them are fine. How do we actually know? Maybe this is the only way we'll ever get to find out…' She rested her hands back on her hips and started to pace. 'I don't care about DNA stuff. I want to know more about the dinosaurs. I'm not sure I believe everything the Stipulators tell us.'

'Oh no.' He waggled his finger at her. 'Don't you start your crusade. I'll tell you exactly how we know they are horrible people-eating monsters. How many people came back last time? Three. Three! Out of a hundred. How many the time before that? Why don't you go and ask Lucca Cran what she thinks about Piloria? She lost her son there three years ago, remember?'

But Storm was still shaking her head. 'I know all that. I know it. But don't you see? This is different. This isn't about searching for new food. This is about killing the dinosaurs – wiping them out. Do we even know what DNA is? We only know what they told us in the city auditorium. Is it safe to tamper with?' She stepped forward so she was face-to-face with Dell. 'Should we even be doing this?' She paused. 'If we go along too we can find out for ourselves what's happening, instead of having to believe everything they want us to believe.'

Dell let out a yell. Any chance they had of keeping this conversation to themselves was instantly blown. 'Why would they be lying?'

By S. M. Wilson

The ABC Murders

He paused. A frown of perplexity creased his forehead. His hands automatically straightened an object or two that I had inadvertently pushed awry.

'I am not sure,' he said slowly.

There was something so odd about his tone that I looked at him in surprise.

The frown still lingered.

Suddenly with a brief decisive nod of the head he crossed the room to a desk near the window. Its contents, I need hardly say, were all neatly docketed and pigeon-holed so that he was able at once to lay his hand upon the paper he wanted.

He came slowly across to me, an open letter in his hand. He read it through himself, then passed it to me.

'Tell me, *mon ami*,' he said. 'What do you make of this?'

I took it from him with some interest.

It was written on thickish white notepaper in printed characters:

Mr Hercule Poirot, – You fancy yourself, don't you, at solving mysteries that are too difficult for our poor thick-headed British police? Let us see, Mr Clever Poirot, just how clever you can be. Perhaps you'll find this nut too hard to crack. Look out for Andover, on the 21st of the month.

Yours, etc.,

ABC.

I glanced at the envelope. That also was printed. 'Postmarked WC1,' said Poirot as I turned my attention to the postmark. 'Well, what is your opinion?'

I shrugged my shoulders as I handed it back to him.

'Some madman or other, I suppose.'

'That is all you have to say?'

'Well – doesn't it sound like a madman to you?'

'Yes, my friend, it does.'

His tone was grave. I looked at him curiously.

'You take this very seriously, Poirot.'

'A madman, *mon ami*, is to be taken seriously. A madman is a very dangerous thing.'

By Agatha Christie

Level 2 Speaking Verse and Prose:
Grade 5 – Verse

Titles in Level 2 Speaking Verse and Prose:
Grade 5 – Verse

The Wolf and the Crane

Love and Friendship

An Irish Airman Foresees His Death

A Bird Came Down the Walk (originally published as In the
  Garden)

The Usual Suspect

Song of the Sirens

Tula ['Books are door-shaped']

Dear Mr Examiner

The Wolf and the Crane

A wolf, once forgetting the size of his swallow,
Tried to pass a large marrow-bone through it.
'Oh dear,' said the beast, thinking death was to follow,
'How careless and stupid to do it!'

His mouth was propp'd open by means of the bone,
And his breathing was greatly impeded,
But a crane coming up, he contrived to make known
What kind of assistance he needed.

'How d'ye do?' said the bird; said the beast, 'Very ill,
For a bone has gone down the wrong way;
But if you can extract it by means of your bill,
The service I'll amply repay.'

Thought the crane, 'I'm no surgeon: yet all must agree,
That my bill will make excellent forceps;
And as for the money, I do not now see
Why I need refuse taking his worship's.'

Said the bird, 'It's agreed;' said his patient, 'Proceed,
And take the bone hence, I beseech;'
Which, after a while, and with infinite toil,
The crane at last managed to reach.

'Thank my stars!' said the beast, from his terrors released,
'Thank you too, sir,' said he to the bird;

'Alas!' said the crane, 'is this all I'm to gain,
I was waiting the promised reward.'

Said the wolf, 'You forget, I've contracted no debt,
Since the service was *rendered by me*;
Your head I releas'd from the jaws of a beast,
And now you're demanding a fee!'

By Marmaduke Park

Love and Friendship

Love is like the wild rose-briar,
Friendship like the holly-tree–
The holly is dark when the rose-briar blooms
But which will bloom most constantly?

The wild rose-briar is sweet in spring,
Its summer blossoms scent the air;
Yet wait till winter comes again
And who will call the wild-briar fair?

Then scorn the silly rose-wreath now
And deck thee with the holly's sheen,
That when December blights thy brow
He still may leave thy garland green.

By Emily Brontë

An Irish Airman Foresees His Death

I know that I shall meet my fate

Somewhere among the clouds above;

Those that I fight I do not hate

Those that I guard I do not love;

My country is Kiltartan Cross,

My countrymen Kiltartan's poor,

No likely end could bring them loss

Or leave them happier than before.

Nor law, nor duty bade me fight,

Nor public man, nor angry crowds,

A lonely impulse of delight

Drove to this tumult in the clouds;

I balanced all, brought all to mind,

The years to come seemed waste of breath,

A waste of breath the years behind

In balance with this life, this death.

By W. B. Yeats

A Bird Came Down the Walk
(originally published as In the Garden)

A bird came down the walk:
He did not know I saw;
He bit an angle worm in halves
And ate the fellow, raw.

And then he drank a dew
From a convenient grass,
And then hopped sidewise to the wall
To let a beetle pass.

He glanced with rapid eyes
That hurried all abroad, –
They looked like frightened beads, I thought;
He stirred his velvet head.

Like one in danger, cautious,
I offered him a crumb,
And he unrolled his feathers,
And rowed him softer home

Than oars divide the ocean,
Too silver for a seam,
Or butterflies, off banks of noon,
Leap, plashless as they swim.

By Emily Dickinson

The Usual Suspect

I'm the demon of the stair,
I'm waiting for you here.
I know you're on the way because
I can smell your fear.

I'm the ghoul beneath the bed
I terrify the meek.
This is my home: I'm always here,
But never when you peek.

I'm the figure in the flame,
The spectre in the smoke.
Wind in the chimney is my voice
Although I never spoke.

I'm the monster in the cupboard,
The face behind the door.
The less you try to think of me
I think of you the more.

And though you might imagine me
As gremlin, imp, or elf,
The truth is ten times worse, because
I am – of course – yourself.

By David Harsent

Song of the Sirens

Come Odysseus draw thou near

Our celestial voice to hear

Weaving notes that intertwine

Gradually will make you mine

Beg your men the boat to stear

Close Odysseus, do not fear

Come Odysseus nearer still

Sail your ship so close until

We may wrap you in our arms

Soothe your worries with our charms

Brave Odysseus fear no ill

From our voices soft not shrill

Come Odysseus faster row

Sluggish sailors go too slow

Once you taste our watery kiss

Die forever in such bliss

We will gently help you go

Sink in to our world below

By Ginny Avery

Tula ['Books are door-shaped']

Books are door-shaped
portals
carrying me
across oceans
and centuries,
helping me feel
less alone.

But my mother believes
that girls who read too much
are unladylike
and ugly,
so my father's books are locked
in a clear glass cabinet. I gaze
at enticing covers
and mysterious titles,
but I am rarely permitted
to touch
the enchantment
of words.

Poems.
Stories.
Plays.
All are forbidden.
Girls are not supposed to think,
but as soon as my eager mind
begins to race, free thoughts
rush in
to replace
the trapped ones.

I imagine distant times
and faraway places.
Ghosts.
Vampires.
Ancient warriors.
Fantasy moves into
the tangled maze
of lonely confusion.

Secretly, I open
an invisible book in my mind,
and I step
through its magical door-shape
into a universe
of dangerous villains
and breathtaking heroes.

Many of the heroes are men
and boys, but some are girls
so tall
strong
and clever
that they rescue other children
from monsters.

By Margarita Engle

Dear Mr Examiner

Thank you so much for your questions
I've read them most carefully through
But there isn't a single one of them
That I know the answer to.

I've written my name as instructed
Put the year, the month and the day
But after I'd finished doing that
I had nothing further to say.

So I thought I'd write you a letter
Fairly informally
About what I can see from my desk here
And what it's like to be me.

Mandy has written ten pages
But it's probably frightful guff
And Angela Smythe is copying
The answers off her cuff.

Miss Quinlan is marking our homework
The clock keeps ticking away
I suppose for anyone outside
It's just another day.

There'll be mothers going on errands
Grandmothers sipping tea
Unemployed men doing crosswords
Or watching 'Crown Court' on TV.

The rain has finally stopped here
The sun has started to shine
And in a back garden in Sefton Drive
A housewife hangs shirts on a line.

A class files past to play tennis
The cathedral clock has just pealed
A mower chugs backwards and forwards
Up on the hockey field.

Miss Quinlan's just read what I've written
Her face is an absolute mask
Before she collects the papers in
I've a sort of favour to ask.

I thought your questions were lovely
I've only myself to blame
But couldn't you give me some marks
For writing the date and my name.

By Gareth Owen

Level 2 Speaking Verse and Prose:
Grade 5 – Prose

Titles in Level 2 Speaking Verse and Prose:
Grade 5 – Prose

Skulduggery Pleasant (Book 1)

North and South

Private Peaceful

The Model Millionaire

The Subtle Knife

Miss Mapp

The Hobbit

Tik-Tok of Oz

Skulduggery Pleasant (Book 1)

She cried out and fell backwards as the vampire burst through the closed section of the skylight, showering her with glass. It hit the roof in a crouch. Stephanie didn't even have time to get to her feet before it dived at her.

She turned away and its claws raked across her coat but didn't penetrate the material, although the impact slammed her to the roof again. The vampire overshot but spun as soon as it landed, snarling. Its fangs dripped with saliva and its eyes locked on to hers.

For a moment neither of them made a move, then Stephanie slowly got to her hands and knees. The vampire hissed, but she didn't break eye contact. She tucked her feet beneath her and squatted. The vampire was waiting for her to make a sudden move. The gun was in her pocket but she didn't go for it.

Stephanie moved slowly. She kept her eyes open, didn't blink, didn't do anything that might give it an excuse to resume its attack. Her knees straightened, though she stayed bent over. She took her first step, to the left. The vampire moved with her.

Its eyes blazed with sheer ferocity. All it wanted to do was rip her apart. All it wanted was her complete and utter annihilation. She forced herself to keep calm.

'Easy boy', she said softly and the vampire snapped at the air. Its claws clicked against themselves. Even though they hadn't pierced her coat, her back was throbbing in pain. She knew that if it hadn't been for whatever material this coat was made from, that single swipe would have killed her.

The vampire began moving towards her. Stephanie started to back away but the moment she tried moving her foot behind her, the vampire's hackles rose. She froze. If it leaped from that distance it would be on her before she knew what was happening. It kept coming, moving slowly, stalking its prey.

By Derek Landy

North and South

At her father's quotation Margaret looked suddenly up, with inquiring wonder in her eyes. How in the world had they got from cog-wheels to Chevy Chace?

'It is no boast of mine,' replied Mr. Thornton; 'it is plain matter-of-fact. I won't deny that I am proud of belonging to a town—or perhaps I should rather say a district—the necessities of which give birth to such grandeur of conception. I would rather be a man toiling, suffering—nay, failing and successless—here, than lead a dull prosperous life in the old worn grooves of what you call more aristocratic society down in the South, with their slow days of careless ease. One may be clogged with honey and unable to rise and fly.'

'You are mistaken,' said Margaret, roused by the aspersion on her beloved South to a fond vehemence of defence, that brought the colour into her cheeks and the angry tears into her eyes. 'You do not know anything about the South. If there is less adventure or less progress—I suppose I must not say less excitement—from the gambling spirit of trade, which seems requisite to force out these wonderful inventions, there is less suffering also. I see men here going about in the streets who look ground down by some pinching sorrow or care—who are not only sufferers but haters. Now, in the South we have our poor, but there is not that terrible expression in their countenances of a sullen sense of injustice which I see here. You do not know the South, Mr. Thornton,' she concluded, collapsing into a determined silence, and angry with herself for having said so much.

'And may I say you do not know the North?' asked he, with an inexpressible gentleness in his tone, as he saw that he had really hurt her.

By Elizabeth Cleghorn Gaskell

Private Peaceful

I am on stand-to the next morning, locked inside my gas mask in a world of my own, listening to myself breathing. The mist rises over no-man's-land. I see in front of me a blasted wasteland. No vestige of fields or trees here, not a blade of grass – simply a land of mud and craters. I see unnatural humps scattered over there beyond our wire. They are the unburied, some in field-grey uniforms and some in khaki. There is one lying in the wire with his arm stretched heavenwards, his hand pointing. He is one of ours, or was. I look up where he is pointing. There are birds up there, and they are singing. I see a beady-eyed blackbird singing to the world from his barbed-wire perch. He has no tree to sing from.

The pipsqueak of a lieutenant says, 'Keep your eyes peeled, lads. Keep your wits about you.' He's always doing that, always telling us to do things we're already doing. But nothing moves out there in no-man's-land but the crows. It is a dead man's land.

We're back down in the dugout after stand-to, brewing up when the bombardment starts. It doesn't stop for two whole days. They are the longest two days of my life. I cower there, we all do, each of us alone in our own private misery. We cannot talk for the din. There can be little sleep. When I do sleep I see the hand pointing skywards, and it is Father's hand, and I wake shaking. Nipper Martin has got the shakes, too, and Pete tries to calm him but he can't. I cry like a baby sometimes and not even Charlie can comfort me. We want nothing more than for it to stop, for the earth to be still again, for there to be quiet. I know that when it's over they'll be coming for us, that I'll have to be ready for them, for the gas maybe, or the flame-thrower, or the grenades, or the bayonets. But I don't mind how they come. Let them come. I just want this to stop. I just want it to be over.

When at last it does we are ordered out on to the firestep, gas masks on, bayonets fixed, eyes straining through the smoke that drifts across in front of us. Then out of the smoke we see them come, their bayonets glinting, one or two at first, but then hundreds, thousands. Charlie's there beside me.

'You'll be alright, Tommo,' he says. 'You'll be fine.'

He knows my thoughts. He sees my terror. He knows I want to run.

By Michael Morpurgo

The Model Millionaire

The old beggar-man took advantage of Trevor's absence to rest for a moment on a wooden bench that was behind him. He looked so forlorn and wretched that Hughie could not help pitying him, and felt in his pockets to see what money he had. All he could find was a sovereign and some coppers. 'Poor old fellow,' he thought to himself, 'he wants it more than I do, but it means no hansoms for a fortnight'; and he walked across the studio and slipped the sovereign into the beggar's hand.

The old man started, and a faint smile flitted across his withered lips. 'Thank you, sir,' he said, 'thank you.'

Then Trevor arrived, and Hughie took his leave, blushing a little at what he had done. He spent the day with Laura, got a charming scolding for his extravagance, and had to walk home.

That night he strolled into the Palette Club about eleven o'clock, and found Trevor sitting by himself in the smoking-room drinking hock and seltzer.

'Well, Alan, did you get the picture finished all right?' he said, as he lit his cigarette.

'Finished and framed, my boy!' answered Trevor; 'and, by the bye, you have made a conquest. That old model you saw is quite devoted to you. I had to tell him all about you—who you are, where you live, what your income is, what prospects you have—'

'My dear Alan,' cried Hughie, 'I shall probably find him waiting for me when I go home. But of course you are only joking. Poor old wretch! I wish I could do something for him. I think it is dreadful that any one should be so miserable. I have got heaps of old clothes at home—do you think he would care for any of them? Why, his rags were falling to bits.'

'But he looks splendid in them,' said Trevor. 'I wouldn't paint him in a frock coat for anything. What you call rags I call romance. What seems poverty to you is picturesqueness to me. However, I'll tell him of your offer.'

'Alan,' said Hughie seriously, 'you painters are a heartless lot.'

'An artist's heart is his head,' replied Trevor; 'and besides, our business is to realise the world as we see it, not to reform it as we know it. And now tell me how Laura is. The old model was quite interested in her.'

'You don't mean to say you talked to him about her?' said Hughie.

'Certainly I did. He knows all about the relentless colonel, the lovely Laura, and the £10,000.'

'You told that old beggar all my private affairs?' cried Hughie, looking very red and angry.

'My dear boy,' said Trevor, smiling, 'that old beggar, as you call him, is one of the richest men in Europe. He could buy all London to-morrow without overdrawing his account. He has a house in every capital, dines off gold plate, and can prevent Russia going to war when he chooses.'

By Oscar Wilde

The Subtle Knife

The house was silent. In the last of the evening light the man across the road was washing his car, but he took no notice of Will, and Will didn't look at him. The less notice people took, the better.

Holding Moxie against his chest, he unlocked the door and went in quickly. Then he listened very carefully before putting her down. There was nothing to hear; the house was empty.

He opened a tin for her and left her to eat in the kitchen. How long before the man came back? There was no way of telling, so he'd better move quickly. He went upstairs and began to search.

He was looking for a battered green leather writing-case. There are a surprising number of places to hide something that size even in any ordinary modern house; you don't need secret panels and extensive cellars in order to make something hard to find. Will searched his mother's bedroom first, ashamed to be looking through the drawers where she kept her underclothes, and then he worked systematically through the rest of the rooms upstairs, even his own. Moxie came to see what he was doing and sat and cleaned herself nearby, for company.

But he didn't find it.

By that time it was dark, and he was hungry. He made himself baked beans on toast and sat at the kitchen table wondering about the best order to look through the downstairs rooms.

As he was finishing his meal, the phone rang.

He sat absolutely still, his heart thumping. He counted: twenty-six rings, and then it stopped. He put his plate in the sink and started to search again.

Four hours later he still hadn't found the green leather case. It was half-past one, and he was exhausted. He lay on his bed fully clothed and fell asleep at once, his dreams tense and crowded, his mother's unhappy frightened face always there just out of reach.

And almost at once, it seemed (though he'd been asleep for nearly three hours) he woke up knowing two things simultaneously.

First, he knew where the case was. And second, he knew that the men were downstairs, opening the kitchen door.

By Philip Pullman

Miss Mapp

'You've got a black heart, Diva!'

'That's nonsense,' said Diva firmly. 'Heart's as red as anybody's, and talking of black hearts doesn't become *you*, Elizabeth. You knew I was cutting out roses from my curtains—'

Miss Mapp laughed shrilly.

'Well, if I happen to notice that you've taken your chintz curtains down,' she said with an awful distinctness that showed the wisdom-teeth of which Diva had got three at the most, 'and pink bunches of roses come flying out of your window into the High Street, even my poor wits, small as they are, are equal to drawing the conclusion that you are cutting roses out of curtains. Your well-known fondness for dress did the rest. With your permission, Diva, I intend to draw exactly what conclusions I please on every occasion, including this one.'

'Ho! That's how you got the idea then,' said Diva. 'I knew you had cribbed it from me.'

'Cribbed?' asked Miss Mapp, in ironical ignorance of what so vulgar and slangy an expression meant.

'Cribbed means taking what isn't yours,' said Diva. 'Even then, if you had only acted in a straightforward manner—'

Miss Mapp, shaken as with palsy, regretted that she had let slip, out of pure childlike joy, in irony, the manner in which she had obtained the poppy-notion, but in a quarrel regrets are useless, and she went on again.

'And would you very kindly explain how or when I have acted in a manner that was not straightforward,' she asked with laborious politeness. 'Or do I understand that a monopoly of cutting up chintz curtains for personal adornment has been bestowed on you by Act of Parliament?'

'You knew I was meaning to make a frock with chintz roses on it,' said Diva. 'You stole my idea. Worked night and day to be first. Just like you. Mean behaviour.'

E. F. Benson

The Hobbit

'That's right,' said Gandalf. 'Let's have no more argument. I have chosen Mr. Baggins and that ought to be enough for all of you. If I say he is a Burglar, a Burglar he is, or will be when the time comes. There is a lot more in him than you guess, and a deal more than he has any idea of himself. You may (possibly) all live to thank me yet. Now Bilbo, my boy, fetch the lamp, and let's have a little light on this!'

On the table in the light of a big lamp with a red shade he spread a piece of parchment rather like a map. 'This was made by Thror, your grandfather, Thorin,' he said in answer to the dwarves' excited questions. 'It is a plan of the Mountain.'

'I don't see that this will help us much,' said Thorin disappointedly after a glance. 'I remember the Mountain well enough and the lands about it. And I know where Mirkwood is, and the Withered Heath where the great dragons bred.'

'There is a dragon marked in red on the Mountain,' said Balin, 'but it will be easy enough to find him without that, if ever we arrive there.'

'There is one point that you haven't noticed,' said the wizard, 'and that is the secret entrance. You see that rune on the West side, and the hand pointing to it from the other runes? That marks a hidden passage to the Lower Halls.' (Look at the map at the beginning of this book, and you will see there the runes in red.)

'It may have been secret once,' said Thorin, 'but how do we know that it is secret any longer? Old Smaug has lived there long enough now to find out anything there is to know about those caves.'

'He may—but he can't have used it for years and years.'

'Why?'

'Because it is too small. "Five feet high the door and three may walk abreast" say the runes, but Smaug could not creep into a hole that size, not even when he was a young dragon, certainly not after devouring so many of the dwarves and men of Dale.'

'It seems a great big hole to me,' squeaked Bilbo (who had no experience of dragons and only of hobbit-holes). He was getting excited and interested again, so that he forgot to keep his mouth shut. He loved maps, and in his hall there hung a large one of the Country Round with all his favourite walks marked on it in red ink. 'How could such a large door be kept secret from everybody outside, apart from the dragon?' he asked. He was only a little hobbit you must remember.

By J. R. R. Tolkien

Tik-Tok of Oz

Now, Ann had not forgotten when her birthday came, for that meant a party and feasting and dancing, but she had quite forgotten how many years the birthdays marked. In a land where people live always, this is not considered a cause for regret, so we may justly say that Queen Ann of Oogaboo was old enough to make jelly—and let it go at that.

But she didn't make jelly, or do any more of the housework than she could help. She was an ambitious woman and constantly resented the fact that her kingdom was so tiny and her people so stupid and unenterprising. Often she wondered what had become of her father and mother, out beyond the pass, in the wonderful Land of Oz, and the fact that they did not return to Oogaboo led Ann to suspect that they had found a better place to live. So, when Salye refused to sweep the floor of the living room in the palace, and Ann would not sweep it, either, she said to her sister: 'I'm going away. This absurd Kingdom of Oogaboo tires me.'

'Go, if you want to,' answered Salye; 'but you are very foolish to leave this place.'

'Why?' asked Ann.

'Because in the Land of Oz, which is Ozma's country, you will be a nobody, while here you are a Queen.'

'Oh, yes! Queen over eighteen men, twenty-seven women and forty-four children!' returned Ann bitterly.

'Well, there are certainly more people than that in the great Land of Oz,' laughed Salye. 'Why don't you raise an army and conquer them, and be Queen of all Oz?' she asked, trying to taunt Ann and so to anger her. Then she made a face at her sister and went into the back yard to swing in the hammock.

Her jeering words, however, had given Queen Ann an idea. She reflected that Oz was reported to be a peaceful country and Ozma a mere girl who ruled with gentleness to all and was obeyed because her people loved her. Even in Oogaboo the story was told that Ozma's sole army consisted of twenty-seven fine officers, who wore beautiful uniforms but carried no weapons, because there was no one to fight. Once there had been a private soldier, besides the officers, but Ozma had made him a

Captain-General and taken away his gun for fear it might accidentally hurt some one.

The more Ann thought about the matter the more she was convinced it would be easy to conquer the Land of Oz and set herself up as Ruler in Ozma's place, if she but had an army to do it with. Afterward she could go out into the world and conquer other lands, and then perhaps she could find a way to the moon, and conquer that. She had a warlike spirit that preferred trouble to idleness.

By L. Frank Baum

Level 3 Speaking Verse and Prose:

Grade 6 – Verse

Titles in Level 3 Speaking Verse and Prose:
Grade 6 – Verse

City of Ships

Those Winter Sundays

[love is more thicker than forget]

A Poison Tree

Friday

Ah, Ah

I am Offering This Poem

It Ain't What You Do It's What It Does To You

City of Ships

City of ships!

(O the black ships! O the fierce ships!

O the beautiful sharp-bow'd steam-ships and sail-ships!)

City of the world! (for all races are here,

All the lands of the earth make contributions here;)

City of the sea! city of hurried and glittering tides!

City whose gleeful tides continually rush or recede, whirling in and out with eddies and foam!

City of wharves and stores—city of tall facades of marble and iron!

Proud and passionate city—mettlesome, mad, extravagant city!

Spring up O city—not for peace alone, but be indeed yourself, warlike!

Fear not—submit to no models but your own O city!

Behold me—incarnate me as I have incarnated you!

I have rejected nothing you offer'd me—whom you adopted I have adopted,

Good or bad I never question you—I love all—I do not condemn anything,

I chant and celebrate all that is yours—yet peace no more,

In peace I chanted peace, but now the drum of war is mine,

War, red war is my song through your streets, O city!

By Walt Whitman

Those Winter Sundays

Sundays too my father got up early
and put his clothes on in the blueblack cold,
then with cracked hands that ached
from labor in the weekday weather made
banked fires blaze. No one ever thanked him.

I'd wake and hear the cold splintering, breaking.
When the rooms were warm, he'd call,
and slowly I would rise and dress,
fearing the chronic angers of that house,

Speaking indifferently to him,
who had driven out the cold
and polished my good shoes as well.
What did I know, what did I know
of love's austere and lonely offices?

By Robert Hayden

[love is more thicker than forget]

love is more thicker than forget
more thinner than recall
more seldom than a wave is wet
more frequent than to fail

it is most mad and moonly
and less it shall unbe
than all the sea which only
is deeper than the sea

love is less always than to win
less never than alive
less bigger than the least begin
less littler than forgive

it is most sane and sunly
and more it cannot die
than all the sky which only
is higher than the sky

By E. E. Cummings

A Poison Tree

I was angry with my friend:

I told my wrath, my wrath did end.

I was angry with my foe:

I told it not, my wrath did grow.

And I waterd it in fears

Night & morning with my tears;

And I sunned it with smiles,

And with soft deceitful wiles.

And it grew both day and night,

Till it bore an apple bright.

And my foe beheld it shine,

And he knew that it was mine.

And into my garden stole,

When the night had veild the pole;

In the morning glad I see;

My foe outstretched beneath the tree.

By William Blake

Friday

The print of a bare foot, the second toe
A little longer than the one which is
Traditionally designated 'great'.
Praxiteles would have admired it.

You must have left in haste; your last wet step
Before boarding your suit and setting sail,
Outlined in talcum on the bathroom floor
Mocks your habitual fastidiousness.

There is no tide here to obliterate
Your oversight. Unless I wipe or sweep
Or suck it up, it will not go away.
The thought delights me. I will keep the footprint.

Too slight, too simply human to be called
Token or promise; I am keeping it
Because it is a precious evidence
That on this island I am not alone.

By Ann Drysdale

Ah, Ah

Ah, ah cries the crow arching toward the heavy sky over the marina.

Lands on the crown of the palm tree.

Ah, ah slaps the urgent cove of ocean swimming through the slips.

We carry canoes to the edge of the salt.

Ah, ah groans the crew with the weight, the winds cutting skin.

We claim our seats. Pelicans perch in the draft for fish.

Ah, ah beats our lungs and we are racing into the waves.

Though there are worlds below us and above us, we are straight ahead.

Ah, ah tattoos the engines of your plane against the sky—away from these waters.

Each paddle stroke follows the curve from reach to loss.

Ah, ah calls the sun from a fishing boat with a pale, yellow sail. We fly by

on our return, over the net of eternity thrown out for stars.

Ah, ah scrapes the hull of my soul. Ah, ah.

By Joy Harjo

I am Offering This Poem

I am offering this poem to you,
since I have nothing else to give.
Keep it like a warm coat
when winter comes to cover you,
or like a pair of thick socks
the cold cannot bite through,

I love you,

I have nothing else to give you,
so it is a pot full of yellow corn
to warm your belly in winter,
it is a scarf for your head, to wear
over your hair, to tie up around your face,

I love you,

Keep it, treasure this as you would
if you were lost, needing direction,
in the wilderness life becomes when mature;
and in the corner of your drawer,
tucked away like a cabin or hogan
in dense trees, come knocking,
and I will answer, give you directions,
and let you warm yourself by this fire,
rest by this fire, and make you feel safe

I love you,

It's all I have to give,

and all anyone needs to live,

and to go on living inside,

when the world outside

no longer cares if you live or die;

remember,

I love you.

By Jimmy Santiago Baca

It Ain't What You Do It's What It Does To You

I have not bummed across America
with only a dollar to spare, one pair
of busted Levi's and a bowie knife.
I have lived with thieves in Manchester.

I have not padded through the Taj Mahal,
barefoot, listening to the space between
each footfall picking up and putting down
its print against the marble floor. But I

skimmed flat stones across Black Moss on a day
so still I could hear each set of ripples
as they crossed. I felt each stone's momentum
spend itself against the water; then sink.

I have not toyed with a parachute cord
while perched on the lip of a light aircraft;
but I held the wobbly head of a boy
at the day centre, and stroked his fat hands.

And I guess that the tightness in the throat
and the tiny cascading sensation
somewhere inside us are both part of that
sense of something else. That feeling, I mean.

By Simon Armitage

Level 3 Speaking Verse and Prose:

Grade 6 – Prose

Titles in Level 3 Speaking Verse and Prose:
Grade 6 – Prose

Marley & Me: Life and Love with the World's Worst Dog

The Maze Runner (Book One)

Frankenstein; or, the Modern Prometheus

My Sister's Keeper

The Bone Sparrow

Washington Square

The Perks of Being a Wallflower

The Adventure of the Mazarin Stone

Marley & Me: Life and Love with the World's Worst Dog

In the summer of 1967, when I was ten years old, my father caved in to my persistent pleas and took me to get my own dog. Together we drove in the family station wagon far into the Michigan countryside to a farm run by a rough-hewn woman and her ancient mother. The farm produced just one commodity — dogs. Dogs of every imaginable size and shape and age and temperament. They had only two things in common: each was a mongrel of unknown and indistinct ancestry, and each was free to a good home. We were at a mutt ranch.

'Now take your time son,' Dad said. 'Your decision today is going to be with you for many years to come.'

I quickly decided the older dogs were somebody else's charity case. I immediately raced to the puppy cage. 'You want to pick one that's not timid,' my father coached. 'Try rattling the cage and see which ones aren't afraid.'

I grabbed the chain-link gate and yanked on it with a loud clang. The dozen or so puppies reeled backward, collapsing on top of one another in a squiggling heap of fur. Just one remained. He was gold with a white blaze on his chest, and he charged the gate, yapping fearlessly. He jumped up and excitedly licked my fingers through the fencing. It was love at first sight.

I brought him home in a cardboard box and named him Shaun. He was one of those dogs that give dogs a good name. He effortlessly mastered every command I taught him and was naturally well behaved. I could drop a crust on the floor and he would not touch it until I gave him the okay. He came when I called him and stayed when I told him to. We could let him out alone at night, knowing he would be back after making his rounds. Not that we often did, but we could leave him alone in the house for hours, confident he wouldn't have an accident or disturb a thing. He raced cars without chasing them and walked beside me without a leash. He could dive to the bottom of our lake and emerge with rocks so big they sometimes got stuck in his jaws. He loved nothing more than riding in the car and would sit quietly in the backseat beside me on family road trips, content to spend hours gazing out the window at the passing world. Perhaps best of all, I trained him to pull me through the neighbourhood dog-sled-style as I sat on my bicycle, making me the hands-down envy of my friends. Never once did he lead me into hazard.

By John Grogan

The Maze Runner (Book One)

He heard noises above—voices—and fear squeezed his chest.

'Look at that shank.'

'How old is he?'

'Looks like a klunk in a T-shirt.'

'You're the klunk, shuck-face.'

'Dude, it smells like *feet* down there!'

'Hope you enjoyed the one-way trip, Greenie.'

'Ain't no ticket back, bro.'

Thomas was hit with a wave of confusion, blistered with panic. The voices were odd, tinged with echo; some of the words were completely foreign—others felt familiar. He willed his eyes to adjust as he squinted towards the light and those speaking. At first he could see only shifting shadows, but they soon turned into the shapes of bodies—people bending over the hole in the ceiling, looking down at him, pointing.

And then, as if the lens of a camera had sharpened its focus, the faces cleared. They were boys, all of them—some young, some older. Thomas didn't know what he'd expected, but seeing those faces puzzled him. They were just teenagers. Kids. Some of his fear melted away, but not enough to calm his racing heart.

Someone lowered a rope from above, the end of it tied into a big loop. Thomas hesitated, then stepped into it with his right foot and clutched the rope as he was yanked toward the sky. Hands reached down, lots of hands, grabbing him by his clothes, pulling him up. The world seemed to spin, a swirling mist of faces and colour and light. A storm of emotions wrenched his gut, twisted and pulled; he wanted to scream, cry, throw up. The chorus of voices had grown silent, but someone spoke as they yanked him over the sharp edge of the dark box. And Thomas knew he'd never forget the words.

'Nice to meet ya, shank,' the boy said. 'Welcome to the Glade.'

By James Dashner

Frankenstein; or, the Modern Prometheus

I suddenly beheld the figure of a man, at some distance, advancing towards me with superhuman speed. He bounded over the crevices in the ice, among which I had walked with caution; his stature, also, as he approached, seemed to exceed that of man. I was troubled; a mist came over my eyes, and I felt a faintness seize me, but I was quickly restored by the cold gale of the mountains. I perceived, as the shape came nearer (sight tremendous and abhorred!) that it was the wretch whom I had created. I trembled with rage and horror, resolving to wait his approach and then close with him in mortal combat. He approached; his countenance bespoke bitter anguish, combined with disdain and malignity, while its unearthly ugliness rendered it almost too horrible for human eyes. But I scarcely observed this; rage and hatred had at first deprived me of utterance, and I recovered only to overwhelm him with words expressive of furious detestation and contempt.

"Devil," I exclaimed, "do you dare approach me? And do not you fear the fierce vengeance of my arm wreaked on your miserable head? Begone, vile insect! Or rather, stay, that I may trample you to dust! And, oh! That I could, with the extinction of your miserable existence, restore those victims whom you have so diabolically murdered!"

"I expected this reception," said the dæmon. "All men hate the wretched; how, then, must I be hated, who am miserable beyond all living things! Yet you, my creator, detest and spurn me, thy creature, to whom thou art bound by ties only dissoluble by the annihilation of one of us. You purpose to kill me. How dare you sport thus with life? Do your duty towards me, and I will do mine towards you and the rest of mankind. If you will comply with my conditions, I will leave them and you at peace; but if you refuse, I will glut the maw of death, until it be satiated with the blood of your remaining friends."

"Abhorred monster! Fiend that thou art! The tortures of hell are too mild a vengeance for thy crimes. Wretched devil! You reproach me with your creation, come on, then, that I may extinguish the spark which I so negligently bestowed."

My rage was without bounds; I sprang on him, impelled by all the feelings which can arm one being against the existence of another.

He easily eluded.

By Mary Wollstonecraft (Godwin) Shelley

My Sister's Keeper

The door bursts open. I practically fall out of my chair and that puts me eye to eye with an incoming German shepherd, which spears me with a look and then marches over to the mug and starts to drink the water inside.

Campbell Alexander comes in, too. He's got black hair and he's at least as tall as my dad – six feet – with a right-angle jaw and eyes that look frozen over. He shrugs out of a suit jacket and hangs it neatly on the back of the door, then yanks a file out of a cabinet before moving to his desk. He never makes eye contact with me, but he starts talking all the same. 'I don't want any Girl Scout cookies,' Campbell Alexander says. 'Although you do get Brownie points for tenacity. Ha.' He smiles at his own joke.

'I'm not selling anything.'

He glances at me curiously, then pushes a button on his phone. 'Kerri,' he says when the secretary answers. 'What is this girl doing in my office?'

'I'm here to retain you,' I say.

The lawyer releases the intercom button. 'I don't think so.'

'You don't even know if I have a case.'

I take a step forward; so does the dog. For the first time I realize it's wearing one of those vests with a red cross on it, like a St Bernard that might carry rum up a snowy mountain. I automatically reach out to pet him. 'Don't,' Alexander says. 'Judge is a service dog.'

My hand goes back to my side. 'But you aren't blind.'

'Thank you for pointing that out to me.'

'So what's the matter with you?'

The minute I say it, I want to take it back. Haven't I watched Kate field this question from hundreds of rude people?

'I have an iron lung,' Campbell Alexander says curtly, 'and the dog keeps me from getting too close to magnets. Now, if you'd do me the exalted honour of leaving, my secretary can find you the name of someone who – '

But I can't go yet. 'Did you really sue God?' I take out all the newspaper clippings; smooth them on the bare desk.

A muscle tics in his cheek, and then he picks up the article lying on top. 'I sued the Diocese of Providence, on behalf of a kid in one of their orphanages who needed an experimental treatment involving fetal tissue, which they felt violated Vatican II. However, it makes a much better headline to say that a nine-year-old is suing God for being stuck with the short end of the straw in life.' I just stare at him. 'Dylan Jerome,' the lawyer admits, 'wanted to sue God for not caring enough about him.'

A rainbow might as well have cracked down the middle of that big mahogany desk. 'Mr Alexander,' I say, 'my sister has leukaemia.'

By Jodi Picoult

The Bone Sparrow

'Are you listening to the sound of the sea?' I ask. 'I'm listening to the stories of the sea. Do you want me to tell you what I hear?'

And now there are at least ten other kids, all gathered round, listening to Eli tell. 'A long way back, when the world was nothing but sea, there lived a whale. The biggest, hugest whale in the ocean. The whale was as old as the universe and as big as this whole country. Every night, the whale would rise to the surface and sing his song to the moon. One night . . .'

And all of us sit, Eli's story wriggling its way so deep into our brains that it can't ever fall out.

Later, I let Queeny have a listen to my shell. 'What am I listening to?' she says, the bored all over her face from my telling. 'The only thing I can hear is air swishing about.'

'That's the sound of the sea,' I tell her.

She just looks back at me. 'Pft. The sea sounds nothing like that.'

And when I show Maá, she takes the shell and listens too. She listens for a long time, and that ache in her eyes gets even louder than ever before. She doesn't say anything, but I can tell from her face that she hears something. 'Later, né?' she says, her voice all low and soft like just thinking is too hard. That's how she talks mostly now.

I hide my shell, along with all the other treasures the Night Sea has washed up, down under Maá's spare shirt and trousers, where no one else will look. But just before I do, I put the shell to my ear and listen again, real hard. I'm pretty sure I can hear just the whisper of my ba's voice in there. Calling out to me. Telling me he's on his way. Telling me that it's not much longer now, because it's already been nine whole years and that's a long time to wait for a ba to come on by.

Someday, it whispers. And the sound of the whisper is as brilliant as a thousand stars being born. I don't tell anyone I heard him, though. Not even Eli.

By Zana Fraillon

Washington Square

'You see, people forget you,' he said, smiling at Catherine with his delightful gaze, while he leaned forward obliquely, turning towards her, with his elbows on his knees.

It seemed to Catherine that no one who had once seen him would ever forget him; but though she made this reflexion she kept it to herself, almost as you would keep something precious.

They sat there for some time. He was very amusing. He asked her about the people that were near them; he tried to guess who some of them were, and he made the most laughable mistakes. He criticised them very freely, in a positive, off-hand way. Catherine had never heard any one—especially any young man— talk just like that. It was the way a young man might talk in a novel; or better still, in a play, on the stage, close before the footlights, looking at the audience, and with every one looking at him, so that you wondered at his presence of mind. And yet Mr. Townsend was not like an actor; he seemed so sincere, so natural. This was very interesting; but in the midst of it Marian Almond came pushing through the crowd, with a little ironical cry, when she found these young people still together, which made every one turn round, and cost Catherine a conscious blush. Marian broke up their talk, and told Mr. Townsend—whom she treated as if she were already married, and he had become her cousin—to run away to her mother, who had been wishing for the last half-hour to introduce him to Mr. Almond.

'We shall meet again!' he said to Catherine as he left her, and Catherine thought it a very original speech.

Her cousin took her by the arm, and made her walk about. 'I needn't ask you what you think of Morris!' the young girl exclaimed.

'Is that his name?'

'I don't ask you what you think of his name, but what you think of himself,' said Marian.

'Oh, nothing particular!' Catherine answered, dissembling for the first time in her life.

'I have half a mind to tell him that!' cried Marian. 'It will do him good. He's so terribly conceited.'

'Conceited?' said Catherine, staring.

'So Arthur says, and Arthur knows about him.'

'Oh, don't tell him!' Catherine murmured imploringly.

'Don't tell him he's conceited? I have told him so a dozen times.'

At this profession of audacity Catherine looked down at her little companion in amazement. She supposed it was because Marian was going to be married that she took so much on herself; but she wondered too, whether, when she herself should become engaged, such exploits would be expected of her.

By Henry James

The Perks of Being a Wallflower

The thing is, when my brother does call home, he doesn't say a lot. He talks about his classes a little bit, but mostly he talks about the football team. There is a lot of attention on the team because they are very good, and they have some really big players. My brother said that one of the guys will probably be a millionaire someday, but that he is 'dumb as a post.' I guess that's pretty dumb.

My brother told this one story where the whole team was sitting around the locker room, talking about all the stuff they had to do to get into college football. They finally got around to talking about SAT scores, which I have never taken.

And this guy said, 'I got a 710.'

And my brother said, 'Math or verbal?'

And the guy said, 'Huh?'

And the whole team laughed.

I always wanted to be on a sports team like that. I'm not exactly sure why, but I always thought it would be fun to have 'glory days.' Then, I would have stories to tell my children and golf buddies. I guess I could tell people about *Punk Rocky* and walking home from school and things like that. Maybe these are my glory days, and I'm not even realizing it because they don't involve a ball.

I used to play sports when I was little, and I was actually very good, but the problem was that it used to make me too aggressive, so the doctors told my mom I would have to stop.

My dad had glory days once. I've seen pictures of him when he was young. He was a very handsome man. I don't know any other way to put it. He looked like all old pictures look. Old pictures look very rugged and young, and the people in the photographs always seem a lot happier than you are.

My mother looks beautiful in old pictures. She actually looks more beautiful than anyone except maybe Sam. Sometimes, I look at my parents now and wonder what happened to make them the way they are. And then I wonder what will happen to my sister when her boyfriend graduates from law school. And what my brother's face will look like on a football card, or what it will look like if it is never on a football card.

By Stephen Chbosky

The Adventure of the Mazarin Stone

It was pleasant for Dr. Watson to find himself once more in the untidy room of the first floor in Baker Street which had been the starting-point of so many remarkable adventures. He looked round him at the scientific charts upon the wall, the acid-charred bench of chemicals, the violin-case leaning in the corner, the coal-scuttle, which contained of old the pipes and tobacco. Finally, his eyes came round to the fresh and smiling face of Billy, the young but very wise and tactful page, who had helped a little to fill up the gap of loneliness and isolation which surrounded the saturnine figure of the great detective.

'It all seems very unchanged, Billy. You don't change, either. I hope the same can be said of him?'

Billy glanced with some solicitude at the closed door of the bedroom.

'I think he's in bed and asleep,' he said.

It was seven in the evening of a lovely summer's day, but Dr. Watson was sufficiently familiar with the irregularity of his old friend's hours to feel no surprise at the idea.

'That means a case, I suppose?'

'Yes, sir, he is very hard at it just now. I'm frightened for his health. He gets paler and thinner, and he eats nothing. 'When will you be pleased to dine, Mr. Holmes?' Mrs. Hudson asked. 'Seven-thirty, the day after to-morrow,' said he. You know his way when he is keen on a case.'

'Yes, Billy, I know.'

'He's following someone. Yesterday he was out as a workman looking for a job. To-day he was an old woman. Fairly took me in, he did, and I ought to know his ways by now.' Billy pointed with a grin to a very baggy parasol which leaned against the sofa. 'That's part of the old woman's outfit,' he said.

'But what is it all about, Billy?'

Billy sank his voice, as one who discusses great secrets of State. 'I don't mind telling you, sir, but it should go no farther. It's this case of the Crown diamond.'

'What – the hundred-thousand-pound burglary?'

By Arthur Conan Doyle

Level 3 Speaking Verse and Prose:
Grade 7 – Verse

Titles in Level 3 Speaking Verse and Prose:
Grade 7 – Verse

The Football Phone-In

The second time that my Dad lost his hair
we'd speak about football over the phone,
my hand on the arm of the fake leather chair
where I'd sit through the nights in my bedroom alone.

I'd ring every Sunday and spin him some lies
like 'dinner was fine' and he'd tell me some too
then we'd talk about Gerrard and feign our surprise
at his plans for LA when the season was through.

See football was safe. We both knew the score.
We could talk about losses for hours at length
but no matter the outcome – a win or a draw–
we could gather some hope and turn it to strength.

You could trust that. Sometimes I think the world
would have to end for football to die.
A nuclear bomb tears through banners unfurled
on the kop end and plumes like a flare through the sky

But were that to happen, I'd still have it here.
Being pulled up the stand, held tight in his arm
through the noise and me grinning from ear to ear.
My Dad and his pride. The warmth in his palm.

So to sit on those Sundays and speak through a phone,

it never seemed hard to pretend that my heart wasn't breaking.

Though I never said it, I'm sure it was known;

he could call me whenever, and he'd never walk alone.

By Benjamin Bridson

(LAMDA Graduate)

Smiles

Smile a little, smile a little,

As you go along,

Not alone when life is pleasant,

But when things go wrong.

Care delights to see you frowning,

Loves to hear you sigh;

Turn a smiling face upon her–

Quick the dame will fly.

Smile a little, smile a little,

All along the road;

Every life must have its burden,

Every heart its load.

Why sit down in gloom and darkness

With your grief to sup?

As you drink Fate's bitter tonic,

Smile across the cup.

Smile upon the troubled pilgrims

Whom you pass and meet;

Frowns are thorns, and smiles are blossoms

Oft for weary feet.

Do not make the way seem harder

By a sullen face;

Smile a little, smile a little,

Brighten up the place.

Smile upon your undone labour;

Not for one who grieves

O'er his task waits wealth or glory;

He who smiles achieves.

Though you meet with loss and sorrow

In the passing years,

Smile a little, smile a little,

Even through your tears.

By Ella Wheeler Wilcox

After I Wake Up

After I wake up and before I get up
I lie in bed each day and think: Supposing,
Only supposing, the leader of some country,
Some party, union, faction, should stand up,
Rise on his hind legs in a public manner,
Get out his sheaf of notes, adjust his glasses,
Sip at his tumbler, hem and haw a little,
Then address his opposition:

Gentlemen,

Gentlemen, we were wrong, we have much wronged you,
The quarrel was of our seeking and our cause,
We owed you thanks and paid you with resentment,
Some truths we hid and others we perverted,
The abstract words we used were always empty.

Gentlemen,

Gentlemen, we were wrong and with full knowledge
And have no right to count upon forgiveness:
Yet we are human, yet we are both human—
Though you were right, our quarrel grew from difference
And in that difference lies the birth of richness
As well as of dispute. Let us exchange then,
And build together what we broke together,

Gentlemen,
And live in peace before eternal darkness.

I dream of that awhile, then sick at heart
Go down to find the newspaper on the mat.

By Hilary Corke

The Life of a Digger

Henry from the island of Jamaica

Jamaican digging crews have to sleep
eighty men to a room, in huge warehouses
like the ones where big wooden crates
of dynamite are stored.

My hands feel like scorpion claws,
clamped on to a hard hard shovel all day,
then curled into fists at night.

At dawn, the steaming labor trains
deliver us by the thousands, down into
that snake pit where we dig
until my muscles feel
as weak as water
and my backbone
is like shattered glass.

But only half the day
is over.

At lunchtime, we see sunburned
American engineers and foremen
eating at tables, in shady tents
with the flaps left open,
so that we have to watch

how they sit on nice chairs,

looking restful.

We also watch the medium-dark

Spanish men, relaxing as they sit

on their train tracks, grinning

as if they know secrets.

We have no place to sit. Not even

a stool. So we stand, plates in hand,

uncomfortable

and undignified.

Back home, I used to dream of saving

enough Panama money

to buy a bit of good farmland

for Momma and my little brothers

and sisters, so that we would all

have plenty to eat.

Now all I want is a chair.

And food with some spice.

And fair treatment.

Justice.

By Margarita Engle

Valentine

Not a red rose or a satin heart.

I give you an onion.
It is a moon wrapped in brown paper.
It promises light
like the careful undressing of love.

Here.
It will blind you with tears
like a lover.
It will make your reflection
a wobbling photo of grief.

I am trying to be truthful.

Not a cute card or a kissogram.

I give you an onion.
Its fierce kiss will stay on your lips,
possessive and faithful
as we are,
for as long as we are.

Take it.
Its platinum loops shrink to a wedding-ring,
if you like.

Lethal.

Its scent will cling to your fingers,

cling to your knife.

By Carol Ann Duffy

You are Old, Father William

'You are old, Father William,' the young man said,

'And your hair has become very white;

And yet you incessantly stand on your head –

Do you think, at your age, it is right?'

'In my youth,' Father William replied to his son,

'I feared it might injure the brain;

But, now that I'm perfectly sure I have none,

Why, I do it again and again.'

'You are old,' said the youth, 'as I mentioned before,

And have grown most uncommonly fat;

Yet you turned a back-somersault in at the door –

Pray, what is the reason of that?'

'In my youth,' said the sage, as he shook his grey locks,

'I kept all my limbs very supple

By the use of this ointment – one shilling the box –

Allow me to sell you a couple?'

'You are old,' said the youth, 'and your jaws are too weak

For anything tougher than suet;

Yet you finished the goose, with the bones and the beak –

Pray, how did you manage to do it?'

'In my youth,' said his father, 'I took to the law,

And argued each case with my wife;

And the muscular strength, which it gave to my jaw,
Has lasted the rest of my life.'

'You are old,' said the youth, 'one would hardly suppose
That your eye was as steady as ever;
Yet you balanced an eel on the end of your nose –
What made you so awfully clever?'

'I have answered three questions, and that is enough,'
Said his father; 'don't give yourself airs!
Do you think I can listen all day to such stuff?
Be off, or I'll kick you down stairs!'

By Lewis Carroll

Parting

There's no use in weeping,
Though we are condemned to part:
There's such a thing as keeping
A remembrance in one's heart:

There's such a thing as dwelling
On the thought ourselves have nursed,
And with scorn and courage telling
The world to do its worst.

We'll not let its follies grieve us,
We'll just take them as they come;
And then every day will leave us
A merry laugh for home.

When we've left each friend and brother,
When we're parted wide and far,
We will think of one another,
As even better than we are.

Every glorious sight above us,
Every pleasant sight beneath,
We'll connect with those that love us,
Whom we truly love till death!

In the evening, when we're sitting
By the fire, perchance alone,

Then shall heart with warm heart meeting,

Give responsive tone for tone.

We can burst the bonds which chain us,

Which cold human hands have wrought,

And where none shall dare restrain us

We can meet again, in thought.

So there's no use in weeping,

Bear a cheerful spirit still;

Never doubt that Fate is keeping

Future good for present ill!

By Charlotte Brontë

Lifted

The land says – *come uphill*: and water says
I will. But take it slow.

A workman's ask and nothing fancy –
Will you? Here's an answer, engineered.

A leisurely machine, a box of oak and stone;
the mitred lock, the water's *YES*.

We're stopped. The bow bumps softly
at the bottom gate, and drifts.

All water wants, all water ever wants,
is to fall. So, we use the fall to lift us,

make of water its own tool, as simple
as a crowbar or a well-tied knot;

open up the paddles, let it dam and pucker,
lift and with it, lift us like a bride, a kite,

a wanted answer, breath no longer held
or like a boat. We're on our way

and rising. Water rushes in like fools;
these tonnages that slip across the cill,

all dirty-bottle green and gathering, into
a giddy hurl then slower, slow until

it ends in glassy bulges, hints of aftermath:
a cool and thorough spending.

Wait, then, for the shudder in the gate,
the backward-drifting boat that tells you

there and here are equal, an imbalance
righted. Ask of water, *help me rise*

and water says: *I will.*

By Jo Bell

Level 3 Speaking Verse and Prose:
Grade 7 – Prose

Titles in Level 3 Speaking Verse and Prose:
Grade 7 – Prose

Go Set a Watchman

The King's Speech

The War of the Worlds

The Book Thief

The Black Tulip

The Dragon's Blade: The Reborn King

Northanger Abbey

The Fault in our Stars

Go Set a Watchman

Atticus Finch shot his left cuff, then cautiously pushed it back. One-forty. On some days he wore two watches: he wore two this day, an ancient watch and chain his children had cut their teeth on, and a wristwatch. The former was habit, the latter was used to tell time when he could not move his fingers enough to dig in his watchpocket. He had been a big man before age and arthritis reduced him to medium size. He was seventy-two last month, but Jean Louise always thought of him as hovering somewhere in his middle fifties—she could not remember him being any younger, and he seemed to grow no older.

In front of the chair in which he was sitting was a steel music stand, and on the stand was *The Strange Case of Alger Hiss*. Atticus leaned forward a little, the better to disapprove of what he was reading. A stranger would not have seen annoyance on Atticus's face, for he seldom expressed it; a friend, however, would expect a dry 'H-rm' to come soon: Atticus's eyebrows were elevated, his mouth was a pleasant thin line.

'H-rm,' he said.

'What, dear?' said his sister.

'I don't understand how a man like this can have the brass to give us his views on the Hiss case. It's like Fenimore Cooper writin' the Waverley Novels.'

'Why, dear?'

'He has a childlike faith in the integrity of civil servants and he seems to think Congress corresponds to their aristocracy. No understanding of American politics a-tall.'

His sister peered at the book's dust jacket. 'I'm not familiar with the author,' she said, thus condemning the book forever. 'Well, don't worry, dear. Shouldn't they be here now?'

'I'm not worrying, Zandra.' Atticus glanced at his sister, amused. She was an impossible woman, but a sight better than having Jean Louise permanently home and miserable. When his daughter was miserable she prowled, and Atticus liked his women to be relaxed, not constantly emptying ashtrays.

He heard a car turn into the driveway, he heard two of its doors slam, then the front door slam. He carefully nudged the music stand away from him with his feet, made one futile attempt to rise from the deep armchair without using his hands, succeeded the second time, and had just balanced himself when Jean Louise was upon him. He suffered her embrace and returned it as best he could.

'Atticus—' she said.

By Harper Lee

The King's Speech

Albert Frederick Arthur George, King of the United Kingdom and the British Dominions and the last Emperor of India, woke up with a start. It was just after 3am. The bedroom in Buckingham Palace he had occupied since becoming monarch five months earlier was normally a haven of peace and quiet in the heart of London, but on this particular morning his slumbers had been rudely interrupted by the crackle of loudspeakers being tested outside on Constitution Hill. 'One of them might have been in our room,' he wrote in his diary. And then, just when he thought he might finally be able to go back to sleep, the marching bands and troops started up.

It was 12 May 1937, and the forty-one-year-old King was about to face one of the greatest – and most nerve-racking – days of his life: his coronation. Traditionally, the ceremony is held eighteen months after the monarch comes to the throne, leaving time not just for all the preparations but also for a decent period of mourning for the previous king or queen. This coronation was different: the date had already been chosen to crown his elder brother, who had become king on the death of their father, George V, in January 1936. Edward VIII had lasted less than a year on the throne, however, after succumbing to the charms of Wallis Simpson, an American divorcee, and it was his younger brother, Albert, Duke of York, who reluctantly succeeded him when he abdicated that December. Albert took the name George VI – as both a tribute to his late father and a sign of continuity with his reign after the upheavals of the previous year that had plunged the British monarchy into one of the greatest crises in its history.

At about the same time, in the considerably less grand setting of Sydenham Hill, in the suburbs of south-east London, a handsome man in his late fifties, with a shock of brown hair and bright blue eyes, was also stirring. He, too, had a big day ahead of him. The Australian-born son of a publican, his name was Lionel Logue and since his first meeting with the future monarch just over a decade earlier, he had occupied a curious but increasingly influential role at the heart of the royal family.

By Mark Logue and Peter Conradi

The War of the Worlds

Most of the spectators had gathered in one or two groups—
one a little crowd towards Woking, the other a knot of people
in the direction of Chobham. Evidently they shared my mental
conflict. There were few near me. One man I approached—he
was, I perceived, a neighbour of mine, though I did not know his
name—and accosted. But it was scarcely a time for articulate
conversation.

'What *ugly brutes*!' he said. 'Good God! What ugly brutes!' He
repeated this over and over again.

'Did you see a man in the pit?' I said; but he made no answer
to that. We became silent, and stood watching for a time side
by side, deriving, I fancy, a certain comfort in one another's
company. Then I shifted my position to a little knoll that gave me
the advantage of a yard or more of elevation and when I looked for
him presently he was walking towards Woking.

The sunset faded to twilight before anything further happened.
The crowd far away on the left, towards Woking, seemed to grow,
and I heard now a faint murmur from it. The little knot of people
towards Chobham dispersed. There was scarcely an intimation of
movement from the pit.

It was this, as much as anything, that gave people courage, and
I suppose the new arrivals from Woking also helped to restore
confidence. At any rate, as the dusk came on a slow, intermittent
movement upon the sand-pits began, a movement that seemed
to gather force as the stillness of the evening about the cylinder
remained unbroken. Vertical black figures in twos and threes
would advance, stop, watch, and advance again, spreading out as
they did so in a thin irregular crescent that promised to enclose
the pit in its attenuated horns. I, too, on my side began to move
towards the pit.

Then I saw some cabmen and others had walked boldly into the
sand-pits, and heard the clatter of hoofs and the gride of wheels.
I saw a lad trundling off the barrow of apples. And then, within
thirty yards of the pit, advancing from the direction of Horsell, I
noted a little black knot of men, the foremost of whom was waving
a white flag.

This was the Deputation. There had been a hasty consultation, and since the Martians were evidently, in spite of their repulsive forms, intelligent creatures, it had been resolved to show them, by approaching them with signals, that we too were intelligent.

Flutter, flutter, went the flag, first to the right, then to the left. It was too far for me to recognise anyone there, but afterwards I learned that Ogilvy, Stent, and Henderson were with others in this attempt at communication. This little group had in its advance dragged inward, so to speak, the circumference of the now almost complete circle of people, and a number of dim black figures followed it at discreet distances.

Suddenly there was a flash of light, and a quantity of luminous greenish smoke came out of the pit in three distinct puffs, which drove up, one after the other, straight into the still air.

By H. G. Wells

The Book Thief

DEATH AND CHOCOLATE

First the colours.

Then the humans.

That's usually how I see things.

Or at least, how I try.

HERE IS A SMALL FACT

You are going to die.

I am in all truthfulness attempting to be cheerful about this whole topic, though most people find themselves hindered in believing me, no matter my protestations. Please, trust me. I most definitely can be cheerful. I can be amiable. Agreeable. Affable. And that's only the As. Just don't ask me to be nice. Nice has nothing to do with me.

REACTION TO THE AFOREMENTIONED FACT

Does this worry you?

I urge you—don't be afraid.

I'm nothing if not fair.

Of course, an introduction.

A beginning.

Where are my manners?

I could introduce myself properly, but it's not really necessary. You will know me well enough and soon enough, depending on a diverse range of variables. It suffices to say that at some point in time, I will be standing over you, as genially as possible. Your soul will be in my arms. A colour will be perched on my shoulder. I will carry you gently away.

At that moment, you will be lying there (I rarely find people standing up). You will be caked in your own body. There might be a discovery; a scream will dribble down the air. The only sound I'll hear after that will be my own breathing, and the sound of the smell, of my footsteps.

The question is, what colour will everything be at that moment when I come for you? What will the sky be saying?

Personally, I like a chocolate-coloured sky. Dark, dark chocolate. People say it suits me. I do, however, try to enjoy every colour I see—the whole spectrum. A billion or so flavours, none of them quite the same, and a sky to slowly suck on. It takes the edge off the stress. It helps me relax.

By Markus Zusak

The Black Tulip

The incident just related was, as the reader has guessed before this, the diabolical work of Mynheer Isaac Boxtel.

It will be remembered that, with the help of his telescope, not even the least detail of the private meeting between Cornelius de Witt and Van Baerle had escaped him. He had, indeed, heard nothing, but he had seen everything, and had rightly concluded that the papers intrusted by the Warden to the Doctor must have been of great importance, as he saw Van Baerle so carefully secreting the parcel in the drawer where he used to keep his most precious bulbs.

The upshot of all this was that when Boxtel, who watched the course of political events much more attentively than his neighbour Cornelius was used to do, heard the news of the brothers De Witt being arrested on a charge of high treason against the States, he thought within his heart that very likely he needed only to say one word, and the godson would be arrested as well as the godfather.

Yet, full of happiness as was Boxtel's heart at the chance, he at first shrank with horror from the idea of informing against a man whom this information might lead to the scaffold.

But there is this terrible thing in evil thoughts, that evil minds soon grow familiar with them.

Besides this, Mynheer Isaac Boxtel encouraged himself with the following sophism:–

'Cornelius de Witt is a bad citizen, as he is charged with high treason, and arrested.

'I, on the contrary, am a good citizen, as I am not charged with anything in the world, as I am as free as the air of heaven.

'If, therefore, Cornelius de Witt is a bad citizen,–of which there can be no doubt, as he is charged with high treason, and arrested,–his accomplice, Cornelius van Baerle, is no less a bad citizen than himself.

'And, as I am a good citizen, and as it is the duty of every good citizen to inform against the bad ones, it is my duty to inform against Cornelius van Baerle.'

Specious as this mode of reasoning might sound, it would not perhaps have taken so complete a hold of Boxtel, nor would he perhaps have yielded to the mere desire of vengeance which was gnawing at his heart, had not the demon of envy been joined with that of cupidity.

Boxtel was quite aware of the progress which Van Baerle had made towards producing the grand black tulip.

By Alexandre Dumas

The Dragon's Blade: The Reborn King

Their whole journey had been in silence. Darnuir sensed that his father was unwilling to engage prematurely in the argument he knew would come. Yet, once down at the harbour, with the bustle of the port all around them, the beating sun intensifying the aromas of fish and seaweed, and the billowing flag of the human's capital ship off on the horizon, Draconess broached the issue.

'Darnuir you know fine well that Aurisha cannot be held.' He spoke so quietly, it was almost a whisper. 'We have to evacuate the city. I gave the order this morning and every ship we have is being prepared to take our people across the sea as we speak. Kasselle won't be troubled to hear this; she is wise and will understand that nothing can be done. Arkus, however, won't be pleased that we are abandoning Aurisha. I will need your help persuading him otherwise.' The King paused for a moment before putting a hand on Darnuir's shoulder. 'Do not fight me on this.'

Darnuir was not at all surprised to hear those words spill from his father's mouth. 'And what, father, is the point of your councils if not to make collective decisions?' He shrugged the hand off his shoulder with a brusque jerk. 'Why bother with this sham? You know my feelings on this matter and you have decided that they count for nothing.'

'Given your other failed judgements, I assumed that you would be more cowed, Darnuir?' Draconess said, quiet but stern. 'In this instance, there was no time for discussion. Scouts returned before dawn: the enemy will be upon us tomorrow, if not before. I had to make a decision in the moment.'

'And you chose to flee.'

'I chose to regroup, and give us a chance to gather our full strength.'

'To what?' Darnuir snapped. 'To have to assault our own city? To have to throw our men against our own defences?'

'No,' Draconess said simply. 'As always, you see through the lens of our people alone.'

'It is our people who will win this war.'

'Since Castallan turned against us and took up residence in the Bastion, we face a war on two fronts, Darnuir.

By Michael R. Miller

Northanger Abbey

The progress of Catherine's unhappiness from the events
of the evening was as follows. It appeared first in a general
dissatisfaction with everybody about her, while she remained in
the rooms, which speedily brought on considerable weariness
and a violent desire to go home. This, on arriving in Pulteney
Street, took the direction of extraordinary hunger, and when that
was appeased, changed into an earnest longing to be in bed;
such was the extreme point of her distress; for when there she
immediately fell into a sound sleep which lasted nine hours, and
from which she awoke perfectly revived, in excellent spirits, with
fresh hopes and fresh schemes. The first wish of her heart was
to improve her acquaintance with Miss Tilney, and almost her
first resolution, to seek her for that purpose, in the pump-room at
noon. In the pump-room, one so newly arrived in Bath must be
met with, and that building she had already found so favourable
for the discovery of female excellence, and the completion of
female intimacy, so admirably adapted for secret discourses and
unlimited confidence, that she was most reasonably encouraged
to expect another friend from within its walls. Her plan for the
morning thus settled, she sat quietly down to her book after
breakfast, resolving to remain in the same place and the same
employment till the clock struck one; and from habitude very little
incommoded by the remarks and ejaculations of Mrs. Allen, whose
vacancy of mind and incapacity for thinking were such, that as she
never talked a great deal, so she could never be entirely silent;
and, therefore, while she sat at her work, if she lost her needle or
broke her thread, if she heard a carriage in the street, or saw a
speck upon her gown, she must observe it aloud, whether there
were anyone at leisure to answer her or not. At about half past
twelve, a remarkably loud rap drew her in haste to the window,
and scarcely had she time to inform Catherine of there being two
open carriages at the door, in the first only a servant, her brother
driving Miss Thorpe in the second, before John Thorpe came
running upstairs, calling out, 'Well, Miss Morland, here I am. Have
you been waiting long? We could not come before; the old devil
of a coachmaker was such an eternity finding out a thing fit to be
got into, and now it is ten thousand to one but they break down
before we are out of the street. How do you do, Mrs. Allen? A
famous ball last night, was not it? Come, Miss Morland, be quick,
for the others are in a confounded hurry to be off. They want to
get their tumble over.'

'What do you mean?' said Catherine. 'Where are you all going to?'

By Jane Austen

The Fault in our Stars

It was unbearable. The whole thing. Every second worse than the last. I just kept thinking about calling him, wondering what would happen, if anyone would answer. In the last weeks, we'd been reduced to spending our time together in recollection, but that was not nothing. The pleasure of remembering had been taken from me, because there was no longer anyone to remember with. It felt like losing your co-rememberer meant losing the memory itself, as if the things we'd done were less real and important than they had been hours before.

When you go into the ER, one of the first things they ask you to do is to rate your pain on a scale of one to ten, and from there they decide which drugs to use and how quickly to use them. I'd been asked this question hundreds of times over the years, and I remember once early on when I couldn't get my breath and it felt like my chest was on fire, flames licking the inside of my ribs fighting for a way to burn out of my body, my parents took me to the ER. A nurse asked me about the pain, and I couldn't even speak, so I held up nine fingers.

Later, after they'd given me something, the nurse came in and she was kind of stroking my hand while she took my blood pressure and she said, 'You know how I know you're a fighter? You called a ten a nine.'

But that wasn't quite right. I called it a nine because I was saving my ten. And here it was, the great and terrible ten, slamming me again and again as I lay still and alone in my bed staring at the ceiling, the waves tossing me against the rocks then pulling me back out to sea so they could launch me again into the jagged face of the cliff, leaving me floating face up on the water, undrowned.

Finally I did call him. His phone rang five times and then went to voice mail. 'You've reached the voice mail of Augustus Waters,' he said, the clarion voice I'd fallen for. 'Leave a message.' It beeped. The dead air on the line was so eerie. I just wanted to go back to that secret post-terrestrial third space with him that we visited when we talked on the phone. I waited for that feeling, but it never came. The dead air on the line was no comfort, and finally I hung up.

By John Green

Level 3 Speaking Verse and Prose:
Grade 8 – Verse

Titles in Level 3 Speaking Verse and Prose:
Grade 8 – Verse

Human Family

I note the obvious differences
in the human family.
Some of us are serious,
some thrive on comedy.

Some declare their lives are lived
as true profundity,
and others claim they really live
the real reality.

The variety of our skin tones
can confuse, bemuse, delight,
brown and pink and beige and purple,
tan and blue and white.

I've sailed upon the seven seas
and stopped in every land,
I've seen the wonders of the world
not yet one common man.

I know ten thousand women
called Jane and Mary Jane,
but I've not seen any two
who really were the same.

Mirror twins are different
although their features jibe,
and lovers think quite different thoughts
while lying side by side.

We love and lose in China,
we weep on England's moors,
and laugh and moan in Guinea,
and thrive on Spanish shores.

We seek success in Finland,
are born and die in Maine.
In minor ways we differ,
in major we're the same.

I note the obvious differences
between each sort and type,
but we are more alike, my friends,
than we are unalike.

We are more alike, my friends,
than we are unalike.

We are more alike, my friends,
than we are unalike.

By Maya Angelou

The Thing about Symmetry

When I appraised the bump on my nose or the freckle on my right
cheek

your eyes would glow behind me, softening the sharp edges of my
mirror

Real beauty is never found in symmetry, you said

My rolling eyes sent ripples through the harsh reflection

but you were never swayed by my tides

You told me: symmetry is for statues

Too perfect to touch

Love is lopsided

It enters in the crooked slope of your lower lip

and settles in the hidden dimple on your back

True beauty is not the equal spacing of the eyes

or the straight alignment of the teeth

It is the flair of your left nostril when you laugh

It is the defects I refuse to upgrade for a model woman.

You hate the irregular spread of your toes

but I have never seen anything so intimate

as the secret flaws you trust me to keep

And when I stare while you sleep

the strands of your fringe drift in the breeze of my breath,

their lengths perfectly unequal

It does not matter that your features are uneven

because so are my hands

and when we touch our bodies are a harmony of imperfections

You turned me away from the mirror

Until the only reflection I saw was in your eyes

Until I saw the beauty in my clumsily scattered freckles

Until I learned to love lopsided

But when you left and slammed the door

you knocked a picture askew

And I have never seen anything so ugly

By Alessandra Davison

(LAMDA Graduate)

Letter to a City under Siege

Turning the pages of the book you have lent me of your wounded city,

reading the Braille of its walls, walking beneath ghost branches

and chestnuts, fires that turn the bullet-shattered windows bronze,

flaring an instant without warming the fallen houses

where you sleep without water or light, a biscuit tin of nothing between you,

or later in the cafe that is no longer, you choose the one,

hours of an evening discussing burnt literature

from the library where all books meet with despair,

I want to give your notes back to you, so they might be

published in a common language, not yours or mine, but a tongue

understood by kindergarteners and night-watchmen.

I want to lie down in the cemetery where violets grow in your childhood

before snipers fired on the city using gravestones for cover.

It isn't difficult to sleep among the dead.

Before leaving I want to tell you that your tunnel is still there,

mud-walled and hallowed of earth, through which you brought

into the city medicine and oranges—oranges!—

bright as winter moons by the barrow-load.

I would crawl through your tunnel as you did,

leaving some of your violets and the night of your poems.

I would bring everyone a gift of pears,

then walk further up, up through the County Street,

where one can see the city in fog, roofs woven of blackened timber, filled with sky, uprooted bridge railings groaning in wind, where a shard of glass is suspended

as a guillotine over the spines of books in a shop window,

and where, through snow, a dog finds his way with, in his mouth, a human bone.

What happens isn't complicated, is it? Nor is the city hell on earth.

Shells don't rain down from the heavens, but are fired by human hands.

The children of the city make bullet-proof vests out of cardboard.

There is no shortage of food, water, medicine—

food, water, medicine are withheld.

The clopping sounds aren't horses, but roof tiles shattering.

There are carcasses of trolley cars, and trams—limbless caryatids.

The library burns on page sixty, as it burns in all the newspapers of the world.

Quiet are the ruins of the houses of God. All the houses.

And what else, what more? No food no light no water.

Clocks aren't spared. The tunnel! The oranges!

By Carolyn Forché

Dulce et Decorum est

Bent double, like old beggars under sacks,
Knock-kneed, coughing like hags, we cursed through sludge,
Till on the haunting flares we turned our backs,
And towards our distant rest began to trudge.
Men marched asleep. Many had lost their boots,
But limped on, blood-shod. All went lame; all blind;
Drunk with fatigue; deaf even to the hoots
Of gas-shells dropping softly behind.

Gas! GAS! Quick, boys!—An ecstasy of fumbling
Fitting the clumsy helmets just in time,
But someone still was yelling out and stumbling
And flound'ring like a man in fire or lime.–
Dim through the misty panes and thick green light,
As under a green sea, I saw him drowning.

In all my dreams before my helpless sight,
He plunges at me, guttering, choking, drowning.

If in some smothering dreams, you too could pace
Behind the wagon that we flung him in,
And watch the white eyes writhing in his face,
His hanging face, like a devil's sick of sin;
If you could hear, at every jolt, the blood
Come gargling from the froth-corrupted lungs,
Obscene as cancer, bitter as the cud
Of vile, incurable sores on innocent tongues,–

My friend, you would not tell with such high zest

To children ardent for some desperate glory,

The old Lie: *Dulce et decorum est*

Pro patria mori.

By Wilfred Owen

The Quangle Wangle's Hat

On the top of the Crumpetty Tree
    The Quangle Wangle sat,
But his face you could not see,
    On account of his Beaver Hat.
For his Hat was a hundred and two feet wide,
With ribbons and bibbons on every side,
And bells, and buttons, and loops, and lace,
So that nobody ever could see the face
      Of the Quangle Wangle Quee.

The Quangle Wangle said
    To himself on the Crumpetty Tree,
'Jam; and jelly; and bread
    Are the best of food for me!
But the longer I live on this Crumpetty Tree
The plainer than ever it seems to me
That very few people come this way
And that life on the whole is far from gay!'
      Said the Quangle Wangle Quee.

But there came to the Crumpetty Tree,
    Mr. and Mrs. Canary;
And they said, 'Did ever you see
    Any spot so charmingly airy?
May we build a nest on your lovely Hat?
Mr. Quangle Wangle, grant us that!
O please let us come and build a nest

Of whatever material suits you best,

    Mr. Quangle Wangle Quee!'

And besides, to the Crumpetty Tree

    Came the Stork, the Duck, and the Owl;

The Snail and the Bumble-Bee,

    The Frog and the Fimble Fowl

(The Fimble Fowl, with a corkscrew leg);

And all of them said, 'We humbly beg

We may build our homes on your lovely Hat, –

Mr. Quangle Wangle, grant us that!

    Mr. Quangle Wangle Quee!'

And the Golden Grouse came there,

    And the Pobble who has no toes,

And the small Olympian bear,

    And the Dong with a luminous nose.

And the Blue Baboon who played the Flute,

And the Orient Calf from the Land of Tute,

And the Attery Squash, and the Bisky Bat, –

All came and built on the lovely Hat

    Of the Quangle Wangle Quee.

And the Quangle Wangle said

    To himself on the Crumpetty Tree,

'When all these creatures move

    What a wonderful noise there'll be!'

And at night by the light of the Mulberry moon

They danced to the Flute of the Blue Baboon,

On the broad green leaves of the Crumpetty Tree,

And all were as happy as happy could be,

    With the Quangle Wangle Quee.

By Edward Lear

Woman Skating

A lake sunken among
cedar and black spruce hills;
late afternoon.

On the ice a woman skating,
jacket sudden
red against the white,

concentrating on moving
in perfect circles.

(actually she is my mother, she is
over at the outdoor skating rink
near the cemetery. On three sides
of her there are streets of brown
brick houses; cars go by; on the
fourth side is the park building.
The snow banked around the rink
is grey with soot. She never skates
here. She's wearing a sweater and
faded maroon earmuffs, she has
taken off her gloves)

Now near the horizon
the enlarged pink sun swings down.
Soon it will be zero.

With arms wide the skater

turns, leaving her breath like a diver's

trail of bubbles.

Seeing the ice

as what it is, water:

seeing the months

as they are, the years

in sequence, occuring

underfoot, watching

the miniature human

figure balanced on steel

needles (those compasses

floated in saucers) on time

sustained, above

time circling: miracle

Over all I place

a glass bell

By Margaret Atwood

Bridge

Between here and Colombia
is a pontoon
of fishnet tights filled tight
with star fruit and green, salted mango.

From here to Colombia
is a pageant
of carnivals and parties
and 1am celebrations and girls
in homemade wedding dresses
twirling on their great-great-uncle's toes.

Between here and Colombia
is a green wave
of parrots tumbling in cages no bigger
than their beady, red-glass eyes.

From here to Colombia
is a necklace
of gourds frothing
with brown nameless soups and fried
everything and big bottom ants and
sauces from everywhere and roadkill armadillo.

Between here and Colombia
is a zip line
of stretched elastic marriages
to high school boyfriends.

Between here and Colombia

are stepping stones

of thousands of lost relatives weaving

down hot pavements dangerous with carts

ready to pinch your cheeks and say

You are too thin, what have you been doing?

And I will set out to travel

from here to Colombia

I shall step out

onto the stretched-tight washing line

which links our houses

and wobble onto

the telephone wires

which dangle in the mango trees.

I will ignore the calls from great aunts and great grandmas

great cousins and first cousins,

and hold out the corners of my dancing skirt.

I shall point my jelly sandals

towards the Colombian sun

and dance *cumbia, cumbia* –

until I get there.

By Aisha Borja

These are the Hands

These are the hands

That touch us first

Feel your head

Find the pulse

And make your bed.

These are the hands

That tap your back

Test the skin

Hold your arm

Wheel the bin

Change the bulb

Fix the drip

Pour the jug

Replace your hip.

These are the hands

That fill the bath

Mop the floor

Flick the switch

Soothe the sore

Burn the swabs

Give us a jab

Throw out sharps

Design the lab.

And these are the hands

That stop the leaks

Empty the pan

Wipe the pipes

Carry the can

Clamp the veins

Make the cast

Log the dose

And touch us last.

By Michael Rosen

Level 3 Speaking Verse and Prose:

Grade 8 – Prose

Titles in Level 3 Speaking Verse and Prose:
Grade 8 – Prose

The Tenant of Wildfell Hall

Shakespeare: The World as a Stage

And the Mountains Echoed

The Cask of Amontillado

Never Let Me Go

The Swedish Match

Starter for Ten

The Voyage Out

The Tenant of Wildfell Hall

The next day was Saturday; and, on Sunday, everybody wondered whether or not the fair unknown would profit by the vicar's remonstrance, and come to church. I confess I looked with some interest myself towards the old family pew, appertaining to Wildfell Hall, where the faded crimson cushions and lining had been unpressed and unrenewed so many years, and the grim escutcheons, with their lugubrious borders of rusty black cloth, frowned so sternly from the wall above.

And there I beheld a tall, lady-like figure, clad in black. Her face was towards me, and there was something in it which, once seen, invited me to look again. Her hair was raven black, and disposed in long glossy ringlets, a style of coiffure rather unusual in those days, but always graceful and becoming; her complexion was clear and pale; her eyes I could not see, for, being bent upon her prayer-book, they were concealed by their drooping lids and long black lashes, but the brows above were expressive and well defined; the forehead was lofty and intellectual, the nose, a perfect aquiline and the features, in general, unexceptionable–only there was a slight hollowness about the cheeks and eyes, and the lips, though finely formed, were a little too thin, a little too firmly compressed, and had something about them that betokened, I thought, no very soft or amiable temper; and I said in my heart–'I would rather admire you from this distance, fair lady, than be the partner of your home.'

Just then she happened to raise her eyes, and they met mine; I did not choose to withdraw my gaze, and she turned again to her book, but with a momentary, indefinable expression of quiet scorn, that was inexpressibly provoking to me.

'She thinks me an impudent puppy,' thought I. 'Humph!–she shall change her mind before long, if I think it worthwhile.'

But then it flashed upon me that these were very improper thoughts for a place of worship, and that my behaviour, on the present occasion, was anything but what it ought to be. Previous, however, to directing my mind to the service, I glanced round the church to see if anyone had been observing me;–but no,–all, who were not attending to their prayer-books, were attending to the strange lady,–my good mother and sister among the rest, and Mrs. Wilson and her daughter; and even Eliza Millward was slily glancing from the corners of her eyes towards the object of general attraction. Then she glanced at me, simpered a little, and blushed, modestly looked at her prayer-book, and endeavoured to compose her features.

Here I was transgressing again; and this time I was made sensible of it by a sudden dig in the ribs, from the elbow of my pert brother. For the present, I could only resent the insult by pressing my foot upon his toes, deferring further vengeance till we got out of church.

By Anne Brontë

Shakespeare: The World as a Stage

Few places in history can have been more deadly and desirable at the same time as London in the sixteenth century. Conditions that made life challenging elsewhere were particularly rife in London, where newly arrived sailors and other travellers continually refreshed the city's stock of infectious maladies.

Plague, virtually always present somewhere in the city, flared murderously every ten years or so. Those who could afford to left the cities at every outbreak. This in large part was the reason for the number of royal palaces just outside London – at Richmond, Greenwich, Hampton Court and elsewhere. Public performances of all types – in fact all public gatherings except for church-going – were also banned within seven miles of London each time the death toll in the city reached forty, and that happened a great deal.

In nearly every year for at least two and a half centuries, deaths outnumbered births in London. Only the steady influx of ambitious provincials and Protestant refugees from the Continent kept the population growing – and grow it did, from fifty thousand in 1500 to four times that number by century's end (such figures are of course estimates). By the peak years of Elizabeth's reign, London was one of the great cities of Europe, exceeded in size only by Paris and Naples. In Britain no other place even came close to rivalling it. A single London district like Southwark had more people than Norwich, England's second city. But survival was ever a struggle. Nowhere in the metropolis did life expectancy exceed thirty-five years, and in some poorer districts it was barely twenty-five. The London that William Shakespeare first encountered was overwhelmingly a youthful place.

The bulk of the population was packed into 448 exceedingly cosy areas within the city walls around the Tower of London and St Paul's Cathedral. The walls survive today only in scattered fragments and relic names – notably those of its gateways: Bishopsgate, Cripplegate, Newgate, Aldgate and so on – but the area they once physically bounded is still known as the City of London and remains administratively aloof from the much vaster, but crucially lower-cased, city of London that surrounds it.

By Bill Bryson

And the Mountains Echoed

Abdullah thought back to two winters ago, everything plunged into darkness, the wind coming in around the door, whistling slow and long and loud, and whistling from every little crack in the ceiling. Outside, the village's features obliterated by snow. The nights long and starless, daytime brief, gloomy, the sun rarely out, and then only to make a cameo appearance before it vanished. He remembered Omar's labored cries, then his silence, then Father grimly carving a wooden board with a sickle moon, just like the one above them now, pounding the board into the hard ground burnt with frost at the head of the small grave.

And now autumn's end was in sight once more. Winter was already lurking around the corner, though neither Father nor Parwana spoke about it, as though saying the word might hasten its arrival.

'Father?' he said.

From the other side of the fire, Father gave a soft grunt.

'Will you allow me to help you? Build the guesthouse, I mean.'

Smoke spiraled up from Father's cigarette. He was staring off into the darkness.

'Father?'

Father shifted on the rock where he was seated. 'I suppose you could help mix mortar,' he said.

'I don't know how.'

'I'll show you. You'll learn.'

'What about me?' Pari said.

'You?' Father said slowly. He took a drag of his cigarette and poked at the fire with a stick. Scattered little sparks went dancing up into the blackness. 'You'll be in charge of the water. Make sure we never go thirsty. Because a man can't work if he's thirsty.'

Pari was quiet.

'Father's right,' Abdullah said. He sensed Pari wanted to get her hands dirty, climb down into the mud, and that she was disappointed with the task Father had assigned her. 'Without you fetching us water, we'll never get the guesthouse built.'

Father slid the stick beneath the handle of the teakettle and lifted it from the fire. He set it aside to cool.

'I'll tell you what,' he said. 'You show me you can handle the water job and I'll find you something else to do.'

Pari tilted up her chin and looked at Abdullah, her face lit up with a gapped smile.

He remembered when she was a baby, when she would sleep atop his chest, and he would open his eyes sometimes in the middle of the night and find her grinning silently at him with this same expression.

By Khaled Hosseini

The Cask of Amontillado

The thousand injuries of Fortunato I had borne as I best could, but when he ventured upon insult, I vowed revenge. You, who so well know the nature of my soul, will not suppose, however, that I gave utterance to a threat. *At length* I would be avenged; this was a point definitely settled—but the very definitiveness with which it was resolved, precluded the idea of risk. I must not only punish, but punish with impunity. A wrong is unredressed when retribution overtakes its redresser. It is equally unredressed when the avenger fails to make himself felt as such to him who has done the wrong.

It must be understood that neither by word nor deed had I given Fortunato cause to doubt my good will. I continued, as was my wont, to smile in his face, and he did not perceive that my smile now was at the thought of his immolation.

He had a weak point—this Fortunato—although in other regards he was a man to be respected and even feared. He prided himself on his connoisseurship in wine. Few Italians have the true virtuoso spirit. For the most part their enthusiasm is adopted to suit the time and opportunity—to practise imposture upon the British and Austrian *millionaires*. In painting and gemmary, Fortunato, like his countrymen, was a quack—but in the matter of old wines he was sincere. In this respect I did not differ from him materially: I was skillful in the Italian vintages myself, and bought largely whenever I could.

It was about dusk, one evening during the supreme madness of the carnival season, that I encountered my friend. He accosted me with excessive warmth, for he had been drinking much. The man wore motley. He had on a tight-fitting parti-striped dress, and his head was surmounted by the conical cap and bells. I was so pleased to see him, that I thought I should never have done wringing his hand.

I said to him—'My dear Fortunato, you are luckily met. How remarkably well you are looking to-day! But I have received a pipe of what passes for Amontillado, and I have my doubts.'

'How?' said he. 'Amontillado? A pipe? Impossible! And in the middle of the carnival!'

'I have my doubts,' I replied; 'and I was silly enough to pay the full Amontillado price without consulting you in the matter. You were not to be found, and I was fearful of losing a bargain.'

'Amontillado!'

'I have my doubts.'

'Amontillado!'

'And I must satisfy them.'

'Amontillado!'

'As you are engaged, I am on my way to Luchesi. If anyone has a critical turn, it is he. He will tell me–'

'Luchesi cannot tell Amontillado from Sherry.'

'And yet some fools will have it that his taste is a match for your own.'

'Come, let us go.'

'Whither?'

'To your vaults.'

By Edgar Allan Poe

Never Let Me Go

We hadn't thought much about how Madame herself, or anyone else, would come into it. What I mean is, until then, it had been a pretty light-hearted matter, with a bit of a dare element to it. And it wasn't even as though Madame did anything other than what we predicted she'd do: she just froze and waited for us to pass by. She didn't shriek, or even let out a gasp. But we were all so keenly tuned in to picking up her response, and that's probably why it had such an effect on us. As she came to a halt, I glanced quickly at her face—as did the others, I'm sure. And I can still see it now, the shudder she seemed to be suppressing, the real dread that one of us would accidentally brush against her. And though we just kept on walking, we all felt it; it was like we'd walked from the sun right into chilly shade. Ruth had been right: Madame was afraid of us. But she was afraid of us in the same way someone might be afraid of spiders. We hadn't been ready for that. It had never occurred to us to wonder how we would feel, being seen like that, being the spiders.

By the time we'd crossed the courtyard and reached the grass, we were a very different group from the one that had stood about excitedly waiting for Madame to get out of her car. Hannah looked ready to burst into tears. Even Ruth looked really shaken. Then one of us—I think it was Laura—said:

'If she doesn't like us, why does she want our work? Why doesn't she just leave us alone? Who asks her to come here anyway?'

No one answered, and we carried on over to the pavilion, not saying anything more about what had happened.

Thinking back now, I can see we were just at that age when we knew a few things about ourselves—about who we were, how we were different from our guardians, from the people outside—but hadn't yet understood what any of it meant. I'm sure somewhere in your childhood you too had an experience like ours that day; similar if not in the actual details, then inside, in the feelings. Because it doesn't really matter how well your guardians try to prepare you: all the talks, videos, discussions, warnings, none of that can really bring it home. Not when you're eight years old, and you're all together in a place like Hailsham; when you've got guardians like the ones we had; when the gardeners and the delivery men joke and laugh with you and call you 'sweetheart'.

All the same, some of it must go in somewhere. It must go in, because by the time a moment like that comes along, there's a part of you that's been waiting. Maybe from as early as when you're five or six, there's been a whisper going at the back of your head, saying: 'One day, maybe not so long from now, you'll get to know how it feels.'

By Kazuo Ishiguro

The Swedish Match

(The Story of a Crime)

Two hours later the examining magistrate drove up. Nikolay Yermolaitch Tchubikov (that was the magistrate's name), a tall, thick-set old man of sixty, had been hard at work for a quarter of a century. He was known to the whole district as an honest, intelligent, energetic man, devoted to his work. His invariable companion, assistant, and secretary, a tall young man of six and twenty, called Dyukovsky, arrived on the scene of action with him.

'Is it possible, gentlemen?' Tchubikov began, going into Psyekov's room and rapidly shaking hands with everyone. 'Is it possible? Mark Ivanitch? Murdered? No, it's impossible! Imposs-i-ble!'

'There it is,' sighed the superintendent.

'Merciful heavens! Why I saw him only last Friday. At the fair at Tarabankovo! Saving your presence, I drank a glass of vodka with him!'

'There it is,' the superintendent sighed once more.

They heaved sighs, expressed their horror, drank a glass of tea each, and went to the lodge.

'Make way!' the police inspector shouted to the crowd.

On going into the lodge the examining magistrate first of all set to work to inspect the door into the bedroom. The door turned out to be made of deal, painted yellow, and not to have been tampered with. No special traces that might have served as evidence could be found. They proceeded to break open the door.

'I beg you, gentlemen, who are not concerned, to retire,' said the examining magistrate, when, after long banging and cracking, the door yielded to the axe and the chisel. 'I ask this in the interests of the investigation. . . . Inspector, admit no one!'

Tchubikov, his assistant, and the police superintendent opened the door and hesitatingly, one after the other, walked into the room. The following spectacle met their eyes. In the solitary window stood a big wooden bedstead with an immense feather bed on it. On the rumpled feather bed lay a creased and crumpled quilt. A pillow, in a cotton pillow case—also much creased, was on the floor. On a little table beside the bed lay a silver watch, and silver coins to the value of twenty kopecks. Some sulphur matches lay there too. Except the bed, the table, and a solitary chair, there was no furniture in the room. Looking under the bed, the superintendent saw two dozen empty bottles, an old straw hat, and a jar of vodka. Under the table lay one boot, covered with dust. Taking a look round the room, Tchubikov frowned and flushed crimson.

'The blackguards!' he muttered, clenching his fists.

By Anton Chekhov

Starter for Ten

It's Christmas morning, and the first thing I do when I get up is eat a big bowl of Frosties and turn the telly on. It's about ten o'clock, and *The Wizard of Oz* has already started, so I put it on in the background while Mum and I open each other's presents. Dad's there too, in a way, like Jacob Marley's ghost, dressed like he was in an old Polaroid I have of him, looking weary and sardonic in a burgundy dressing gown, black hair slicked back, wearing new slippers and smoking the packet of fags that I bought and wrapped up for him as a present.

This year Mum's bought me some new vests and the *Collected Works of E. E. Cummings* that I specifically asked for, and which she had to order specially. I check the price on the fly-leaf and feel a twinge of guilt at how expensive it was, a day's wages at least, but I thank her and kiss her on the cheek, and give her my presents in return – a little wicker basket of smellies from the Body Shop, and a second-hand Everyman edition of *Bleak House*.

'What's this then?'

'It's my favourite Dickens. It's brilliant.'

'"Bleak House"? Sounds like *this* house.'

And that just about sets the tone for the day, really. Dickensian.

We're joined for Christmas dinner by Uncle Des. Uncle Des' wife left him for a bloke from her work a couple of years ago now, so Mum invites him round for Christmas dinner every year because he doesn't have much family of his own. Even though he's not my real uncle, just the bloke from three-doors-down, he thinks he's somehow got the right to ruffle my hair and talk to me as if I was twelve years old.

'How ya' doing then, brainbox?' he says, in his children's entertainer voice.

'Fine thank you, Uncle Des.'

'Bloomin' 'eck, don't they teach you how to use a comb at university!' he says, ruffling away. 'Look at the state of you!' – ruffle, ruffle, ruffle – and it occurs to me that this is all pretty rich coming from a forty-five-year-old man with a tight blond perm and a moustache that looks as if it's been cut out from a carpet sample, but I keep quiet because Mum doesn't like me back-chatting to Uncle Des. So I squirm bashfully and count myself lucky that at least this year he isn't pulling fifty-pence pieces out from behind my ear.

By David Nicholls

The Voyage Out

Rachel had other questions on the tip of her tongue; or rather one enormous question, which she did not in the least know how to put into words. The talk appeared too airy to admit of it.

'Please tell me—everything.' That was what she wanted to say. He had drawn apart one little chink and showed astonishing treasures. It seemed to her incredible that a man like that should be willing to talk to her. He had sisters and pets, and once lived in the country. She stirred her tea round and round; the bubbles which swam and clustered in the cup seemed to her like the union of their minds.

The talk meanwhile raced past her, and when Richard suddenly stated in a jocular tone of voice, 'I'm sure Miss Vinrace, now, has secret leanings towards Catholicism,' she had no idea what to answer, and Helen could not help laughing at the start she gave.

However, breakfast was over and Mrs. Dalloway was rising. 'I always think religion's like collecting beetles,' she said, summing up the discussion as she went up the stairs with Helen. 'One person has a passion for black beetles; another hasn't; it's no good arguing about it. What's your black beetle now?'

'I suppose it's my children,' said Helen.

'Ah—that's different,' Clarissa breathed. 'Do tell me. You have a boy, haven't you? Isn't it detestable, leaving them?'

It was as though a blue shadow had fallen across a pool. Their eyes became deeper, and their voices more cordial. Instead of joining them as they began to pace the deck, Rachel was indignant with the prosperous matrons, who made her feel outside their world and motherless, and turning back, she left them abruptly. She slammed the door of her room, and pulled out her music. It was all old music—Bach and Beethoven, Mozart and Purcell—the pages yellow, the engraving rough to the finger. In three minutes she was deep in a very difficult, very classical fugue in A, and over her face came a queer remote impersonal expression of complete absorption and anxious satisfaction. Now she stumbled; now she faltered and had to play the same bar twice over; but an invisible line seemed to string the notes together, from which rose a shape, a building. She was so far absorbed in this work, for it was really difficult to find how all these sounds should stand together, and drew upon the whole of her faculties, that she never heard a knock at the door. It was burst impulsively open, and Mrs. Dalloway stood in the room leaving the door open, so that a strip of the white deck and of the blue sea appeared through the opening. The shape of the Bach fugue crashed to the ground.

'Don't let me interrupt,' Clarissa implored. 'I heard you playing, and I couldn't resist. I adore Bach!'

Rachel flushed and fumbled her fingers in her lap. She stood up awkwardly.

'It's too difficult,' she said.

'But you were playing quite splendidly! I ought to have stayed outside.'

'No,' said Rachel. She slid *Cowper's Letters* and *Wuthering Heights* out of the arm-chair, so that Clarissa was invited to sit there.

By Virginia Woolf

Title Index

Author Index

Copyright and Acknowledgements

by Kate Clanchy. First published 2018 by Picador an imprint of Pan Macmillan. Copyright © Kate Clanchy 2018. Copyright of each of the poems remains with the poets. Reproduced with permission of Pan Macmillan through PLSclear.

Boyne, John *Noah Barleywater Runs Away*, illustrated by Oliver Jeffers. Published by David Fickling Books. Reprinted by permission of The Random House Group Limited copyright © 2010. Excerpt(s) from *Noah Barleywater Runs Away* by John Boyne, text copyright © 2010 by John Boyne. Used by permission of David Fickling Books, an imprint of Random House Children's Books, a division of Penguin Random House LLC. All rights reserved.

Bridson, Benjamin *The Football Phone-In* used by permission of Benjamin Bridson.

Brown, George Mackay *Beachcomber* copyright © 2005 Estate of George Mackay Brown. Reproduced by permission of John Murray Press, a division of Hodder and Stoughton Limited.

Bryson, Bill *Shakespeare: The World as a Stage*. Reprinted by permission of HarperCollins Publishers Ltd. copyright © Bill Bryson 2007. Chapter Three 'The Lost Years, 1585-1592' [pp. 44-5] from *Shakespeare: The World as a Stage* by Bill Bryson. Copyright © 2007 by Bill Bryson. Reprinted by permission of HarperCollins Publishers.

Bunzl, Peter *Moonlocket* published by Jolly Fish Press, reprinted by permission of Jolly Fish Press, an imprint of North Star Editions. Reproduced from *Moonlocket* by Peter Bunzl by permission of Usborne Publishing, 83–85 Saffron Hill, London EC1N 8RT, UK. www.usborne.com Copyright © 2017 Usborne Publishing Ltd.

Carroll, Emma *Letters from the Lighthouse*. Reprinted by permission of Faber and Faber Ltd.

Causley, Charles *Good Morning, Mr Croco-doco-dile* from *Early in the Morning* published by W. W. Norton. Reprinted by permission of David Higham.

Chbosky, Stephen *The Perks of Being a Wallflower*. Copyright © 1999 by Stephen Chbosky. Reprinted with the permission of Gallery Books, a division of Simon & Schuster, Inc. All rights reserved.

Cheney, Martha *The Backwards Bus* reprinted by permission of Evan-Moor Corporation. © Evan-Moor Corporation.

Christie, Agatha *The ABC Murders* Reprinted by permission of HarperCollins Publishers Ltd. copyright © Agatha Christie Limited, 1936.

Engle, Margarita *Tula ['Books are door-shaped']* from *The Lightning
Dreamer: Cuba's Greatest Abolitionist* by Margarita Engle, copyright ©
2013 by Margarita Engle. Reprinted by permission of Houghton Mifflin
Harcourt Publishing Company. All rights reserved.

Farjeon, Eleanor *There isn't Time* from *Silver Sand and Snow*
published by Michael Joseph. Reprinted by permission of David Higham.

Forché, Carolyn *Letter to a City under Siege* from *The Angel of History*
(1994) by Carolyn Forché, published by Bloodaxe Books. *Letter to a
City under Siege* from *The Angel of History* by Carolyn Forché copyright
© 1994 by Carolyn Forché. Reprinted by permission of HarperCollins
Publishers.

Fraillon, Zana *The Bone Sparrow* by Zana Fraillon. Published by Orion
Children's, 2016. Copyright © Zana Fraillon. Reproduced by permission
of the author c/o Rogers, Coleridge & White Ltd., 20 Powis Mews,
London W11 1JN.

Gaiman, Neil *Neverwhere* Text as submitted ['Oy, 'hissed the man...said
the guide'.] from *Neverwhere* by Neil Gaiman. Copyright © 1996, 1997
by Neil Gaiman. Reprinted by permission of HarperCollins Publishers.
Neverwhere by Neil Gaiman. Copyright © 1996, 1997, 2000 Neil
Gaiman. Reproduced by permission of Headline Publishing Group.

Gardner, Lyn *Olivia's First Term* reprinted by permission of Nosy Crow.

Green, John *The Fault in Our Stars* excerpt(s) from *The Fault in
Our Stars* by John Green, copyright © 2012 by John Green. Used by
permission of Dutton Children's Books, an imprint of Penguin Young
Readers Group, a division of Penguin Random House LLC. All rights
reserved.

Greenfield, Eloise *To Catch a Fish* from *Under the Sunday Tree*.
Text copyright © 1988 by Eloise Greenfield. Used by permission of
HarperCollins Publishers.

Grogan, John *Marley & Me: Life and Love with the World's Worst Dog*
copyright © 2007 John Grogan. Reproduced by permission of Hodder
and Stoughton Limited. Excerpt of 448 words ['In the summer of 1967...
never once did he lead me into hazard.'] from *Marley & Me: Life and
Love with the World's Worst Dog* by John Grogan. Copyright © 2005 by
John Grogan. Reprinted by permission of HarperCollins Publishers.

Haddon, Mark *The Curious Incident of the Dog in the Night-Time*
excerpt(s) from *The Curious Incident of the Dog in the Night-Time: A
Novel* by Mark Haddon, copyright © 2003 by Mark Haddon. Used by
permission of Doubleday, an imprint of the Knopf Doubleday Publishing
Group, a division of Penguin Random House LLC. All rights reserved.
From *The Curious Incident of the Dog in the Night-Time* by Mark
Haddon. Published by Jonathan Cape. Reprinted by permission of The
Penguin Random House Group Limited. Copyright © 2003.

Lee, Harper *Go Set a Watchman*. Excerpt from pp.17-19 from *Go Set a Watchman* by Harper Lee. Copyright © 2015 by Harper Lee. Reprinted by permission of HarperCollins Publishers. From *Go Set a Watchman* by Harper Lee. Published by William Heinemann. Reprinted by permission of The Random House Group Limited. © 2015.

Lee, Li-Young *I Ask My Mother to Sing* from *Rose* copyright © 1986 by Li-Young Lee. Reprinted with the permission of The Permission Company, Inc., on behalf of BOA Editions Ltd., www.boaeditions.org

Levin, Neal *Baby Ate a Microchip* used by permission of Neal Levin.

Logue, Mark *The King's Speech* by Mark Logue and Peter Conradi. Copyright © 2010 Mark Logue and Peter Conradi. Reproduced by permission of Quercus Editions Limited.

Macwilliam, Richard *Migration* used by permission of Richard Quilley (pen name Richard Macwilliam).

Magee, Wes *The Red Boat* used by permission of Wes Magee.

Mather, Ray *Schoolspeak* used by permission of Ray Mather (www.raymather.co.uk).

McLeod, Eleanor *Hot Cross Buns* used by permission of Eleanor McLeod.

Miller, Michael R. *The Dragon's Blade: The Reborn King* used by permission of Michael R. Miller.

Millwood Hargrave, Kiran *The Girl of Ink & Stars*. Text copyright © Kiran Millwood Hargrave 2016. Reproduced with permission of Chicken House Ltd. All rights reserved. Excerpt(s) from *The Girl of Ink & Stars* by Kiran Millwood Hargrave, text copyright © 2016 by Kiran Millwood Hargrave. Used by permission of Yearling, an imprint of Random House Children's Books, a division of Penguin Random House LLC. All rights reserved.

Milosz, Czeslaw *Encounter* from *The Collected Poems 1931–1987* by Czeslaw Milosz. Copyright © 1988 by Czeslaw Milosz Royalties, Inc. Reprinted by permission of HarperCollins Publishers.

Milne, A. A. *If I Were King*. Extract from *When We Were Very Young* by A. A. Milne. Text copyright © The Trustees of the Pooh Properties 1924. Published by Egmont UK Ltd. and used with permission. 'If I Were King' by A. A. Milne; from *When We Were Very Young* copyright © 1924 by Penguin Random House LLC. Copyright renewed 1952 by A. A. Milne. Used by permission of Dutton Children's Books, an imprint of Penguin Young Readers Group, a division of Penguin Random House LLC. All rights reserved.

Mitton, Tony *My Hat!* from *My Hat and All That* published by Scholastic. Reprinted by permission of David Higham.

Morpurgo, Michael *Private Peaceful*. Reprinted by permission of HarperCollins Publishers Ltd. Copyright © Michael Morpurgo 2003. Excerpt from *Private Peaceful* by Michael Morpurgo. Copyright © 2005 by Michael Morpurgo. Reprinted by permission of Scholastic Inc.

Zusak, Markus *The Book Thief*. Published by Doubleday. Reprinted by permission of The Random House Group Ltd. copyright © 2007. Excerpt(s) from *The Book Thief* by Markus Zusak, text copyright © 2005 by Markus Zusak. Used by permission of Alfred A. Knopf, an imprint of Random House Children's Books, a division of Penguin Random House LLC. All rights reserved.